Edexcel
GCSE MODULAR MATHEMATICS
Examples and Practice

FOUNDATION

Stage 3

Heinemann

Edexcel
Success through qualifications

About this book

This *Examples and Practice* book is designed to help you get the best possible grade in your Edexcel GCSE maths examination. The authors are senior examiners and coursework moderators and have a good understanding of Edexcel's requirements.

Foundation Stage 3 Examples and Practice covers all the topics that will be tested in your Foundation Stage 3 examination. You can use this book to revise in the run up to your exam, or you can use it throughout the course, alongside the *Edexcel GCSE Maths* Foundation core textbook.

References in the contents list for each section of the book tell you when to find the most relevant paragraph of the specification. For example, NA2a refers to Number and Algebra, paragraph 2, section a.

Helping you prepare for your exam

To help you prepare, each topic offers:
- **Key points** to reinforce the key teaching concepts
- **Teaching references** showing you where the relevant material is covered in both the old and new editions of the *Edexcel GCSE Maths* Foundation core textbook. These references show you where to find full explanations of concepts, and additional worked examples e.g.

  Teaching reference:
  (pp 47–49, section 3.1, 3.2) — The first reference is to the old edition
  pp 53–56, section 3.2, 3.3 — The second reference is to the new edition

  Where material is new to the new specification there is no reference to the old edition textbooks.
- **Worked examples** showing you how to tackle a problem and lay out your answer
- **Exercises** with references showing you which exercises in the *Edexcel GCSE Maths* Foundation core textbook contain similar questions. The first reference, in brackets and italic, is to the old edition. The second reference is to the new edition
- **A summary of key points** so you can check that you have covered all the key concepts

Exam practice and using the answers

An exam style practice paper at the back of the book will help you make sure that you are totally exam-ready. This paper is exactly the same length and standard as your actual Stage 3 exam.

Answers to all the questions are provided at the back of the book. Once you have completed an exercise you can use the answers to check whether you have made any mistakes. You need to show full working in your exam – it isn't enough to write down the answer.

Which edition am I using?

The new editions of the *Edexcel GCSE Maths* core textbooks have yellow cover flashes saying "ideal for the 2001 specification". You can also use the old edition (no yellow cover flash) to help you prepare for your Stage 1 exam.

The terminal papers

The terminal exam papers cover the full range of content given in the specification for all of Stage 3 in each tier. However, you may expect about half of the questions to be on Stage 3 content.

Contents

Heinemann Educational Publishers,
Halley Court, Jordan Hill, Oxford, OX2 8EJ
a division of Reed Educational & Professional Publishing Ltd
Heinemann is a registered trademark of Reed Educational & Professional Publishing Ltd

OXFORD   MELBOURNE   AUCKLAND
JOHANNESBURG   BLANTYRE   GABORONE
IBADAN   PORTSMOUTH NH (USA)   CHICAGO

First published 2002

ISBN 0 435 53553 6

06   05   04   03   02
10   9   8   7   6   5   4   3   2   1

Designed and typeset by Tech-Set Ltd, Gateshead, Tyne and Wear
Cover photo: Stone Picture Library
Cover design by Miller, Craig and Cocking
Printed in the United Kingdom by Scotprint

Acknowledgements
This product includes mapping data licensed from Ordnance Survey® with the permission of the Controller of Her Majesty's Stationery Office, © Crown copyright.
All rights reserved. Licence no. 100000230.
The publishers and authors would like to thank Jean Linsky for her contribution and assistance with the manuscript.

The answers are not the responsibility of Edexcel.

Publishing team	Design	Production	Author team
Editorial	Phil Richards	David Lawrence	Karen Hughes
Sue Bennett	Colette Jacquelin	Jason Wyatt	Trevor Johnson
Lauren Bourque			Peter Jolly
Des Brady			David Kent
Nicholas Georgiou			Keith Pledger
Derek Huby			
Maggie Rumble			
Nick Sample			
Harry Smith			

Tel: 01865 888058 www.heinemann.co.uk

1 Fractions

1.1 Adding and subtracting fractions

■ To add fractions with the same denominator (bottom), add the numerators (tops) then write the answer over the denominator.

Example 1

(a) $\dfrac{2}{5}+\dfrac{1}{5}$

(b) $\dfrac{3}{7}+\dfrac{2}{7}$

(a) Add numerators

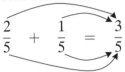

Same denominator

(b) $\dfrac{3}{7}+\dfrac{2}{7}=\dfrac{5}{7}$

■ To add fractions that have different denominators (bottoms), first find equivalent fractions that have the same denominator.

Example 2

Work out $\dfrac{1}{6}+\dfrac{2}{5}$.

> Equivalent fractions are covered in chapter 2 of the Stage 1 Foundation book.

Find equivalent fractions that have the same denominator:

$$\dfrac{1}{6}=\dfrac{2}{12}=\dfrac{3}{18}=\dfrac{4}{24}=\dfrac{5}{30}$$

$$\dfrac{2}{5}=\dfrac{4}{10}=\dfrac{8}{20}=\dfrac{12}{30}$$

$$\dfrac{5}{30}+\dfrac{12}{30}=\dfrac{17}{30}$$

Example 3

Work out $\dfrac{3}{8}+\dfrac{4}{5}$.

An easy way to find equivalent fractions is:

$$\dfrac{3}{8}\ +\ \dfrac{4}{5}$$

$$\dfrac{3\times5}{8\times5}=\dfrac{15}{40}\qquad\dfrac{4\times8}{5\times8}=\dfrac{32}{40}$$

$$\frac{15}{40} + \frac{32}{40} = \frac{47}{40}$$

This is a top-heavy fraction; you usually give answers in their simplest form.

$$\frac{47}{40} = 1\frac{7}{40}$$

Find out about simplifying fractions in chapter 2 of the Stage 1 Foundation book.

Example 4

Work out $\dfrac{3}{4} + \dfrac{5}{12}$.

In this example, notice that 4 is a factor of 12. This means you will only need to change one of the fractions.

$$\frac{3}{4} + \frac{5}{12}$$

$$(12 = 4 \times 3)$$

$$\frac{3 \times 3}{4 \times 3} = \frac{9}{12}$$

$$\frac{9}{12} + \frac{5}{12} = \frac{14}{12}$$

Write $\frac{14}{12}$ in its simplest form:

$$\frac{14}{12} = 1\frac{2}{12} = 1\frac{1}{6}$$

- **To add mixed numbers, first add the whole numbers then add the fractions.**

Example 5

Work out $2\frac{3}{4} + 1\frac{1}{5}$.

First add the whole numbers:

$$2 + 1 = 3$$

Then add the fractions:

$$3\frac{3}{4} + \frac{1}{5} = 3\frac{15}{20} + \frac{4}{20}$$
$$= 3\frac{19}{20}$$

- **To subtract fractions with the same denominator, subtract the numerators, then write the answer over the denominator.**

- **To subtract fractions that have different denominators, first find equivalent fractions that have the same denominator.**

Example 6

Work out:

(a) $\dfrac{4}{7} - \dfrac{2}{7}$ \qquad (b) $\dfrac{3}{4} - \dfrac{2}{5}$ \qquad (c) $\dfrac{5}{8} - \dfrac{7}{16}$

(a) $\dfrac{4}{7} - \dfrac{2}{7}$ (Denominators are the same.)

$= \dfrac{2}{7}$

(b) $\dfrac{3}{④} - \dfrac{2}{⑤}$ (Denominators are different, so find equivalent fractions with the same denominators.)

$\dfrac{3 \times ⑤}{4 \times ⑤} - \dfrac{2 \times ④}{5 \times ④}$

$= \dfrac{15}{20} - \dfrac{8}{20}$

$= \dfrac{7}{20}$

(c) $\dfrac{5}{8} - \dfrac{7}{16}$ (Denominators are different, so find equivalent fractions with the same denominators.)

(Notice $16 = 8 \times 2$)

$\dfrac{5 \times 2}{8 \times 2} = \dfrac{10}{16}$

$\dfrac{10}{16} - \dfrac{7}{16}$

$= \dfrac{3}{16}$

■ **To subtract mixed numbers, first subtract the whole numbers then subtract the fractions.**

Example 7

Work out:

$4\frac{5}{8} - 2\frac{1}{4}$

First subtract whole numbers:

$4 - 2 = 2$

$2\frac{5}{8} - \frac{1}{4} = 2\frac{5}{8} - \frac{2}{8}$

$\qquad = 2\frac{3}{8}$

Exercise 1A   **Links (*4H, 4I*) 4H, 4I**

1 Work out:
  (a) $\frac{2}{5} + \frac{1}{5}$ **(b)** $\frac{3}{7} + \frac{2}{7}$ **(c)** $\frac{3}{12} + \frac{5}{12}$ **(d)** $\frac{5}{8} - \frac{3}{8}$ **(e)** $\frac{7}{10} - \frac{3}{10}$
  (f) $\frac{5}{9} - \frac{2}{9}$ **(g)** $\frac{4}{5} + \frac{2}{5}$ **(h)** $\frac{5}{6} + \frac{5}{6}$ **(i)** $\frac{7}{10} + \frac{5}{10}$ **(j)** $\frac{3}{4} + \frac{1}{4}$

2 Work out:

(a) $\frac{3}{4} + \frac{1}{2}$ (b) $\frac{5}{8} + \frac{3}{4}$ (c) $\frac{5}{7} + \frac{11}{14}$

(d) $\frac{3}{4} - \frac{1}{2}$ (e) $\frac{5}{7} - \frac{3}{14}$ (f) $\frac{13}{20} - \frac{2}{5}$

(g) $\frac{2}{3} + \frac{1}{4}$ (h) $\frac{3}{4} + \frac{2}{5}$ (i) $\frac{5}{8} + \frac{1}{3}$

(j) $\frac{2}{3} - \frac{1}{4}$ (k) $\frac{4}{5} - \frac{2}{3}$ (l) $\frac{7}{8} - \frac{1}{5}$

(m) $\frac{7}{20} + \frac{1}{3}$ (n) $\frac{2}{11} + \frac{5}{7}$ (o) $\frac{11}{13} + \frac{3}{4}$

(p) $\frac{6}{7} - \frac{4}{9}$ (q) $\frac{8}{13} - \frac{2}{5}$ (r) $\frac{13}{15} - \frac{3}{4}$

3 Work out:

(a) $2\frac{1}{4} + 1\frac{3}{4}$ (b) $4\frac{1}{5} + 1\frac{3}{5}$ (c) $2\frac{4}{7} + 3\frac{1}{7}$ (d) $4\frac{5}{8} - 1\frac{3}{8}$

(e) $5\frac{3}{4} - 2\frac{1}{4}$ (f) $2\frac{5}{8} - 1\frac{3}{8}$ (g) $4\frac{1}{4} + 2\frac{1}{2}$ (h) $1\frac{2}{5} + 2\frac{3}{10}$

(i) $2\frac{5}{8} - 1\frac{1}{4}$ (j) $5\frac{1}{3} - 2\frac{4}{15}$ (k) $2\frac{3}{5} + 1\frac{1}{7}$ (l) $3\frac{2}{3} + 1\frac{2}{7}$

(m) $3\frac{6}{7} - 1\frac{2}{3}$ (n) $5\frac{7}{8} - 2\frac{2}{5}$

4 Mrs Rodgers buys $\frac{3}{4}$ kg of apples and $\frac{1}{2}$ kg of pears.
Work out the total weight of the fruit Mrs Rodgers buys.

5 To make a dress the dressmaker requires $\frac{3}{4}$ yards of material to make the bodice and $2\frac{1}{8}$ yards of material to make the skirt. Work out the total amount of material needed to make the dress.

6 In a bag of sweets $\frac{2}{5}$ of the sweets are red and $\frac{1}{6}$ of the sweets are green.
(a) What fraction of the bag of sweets is either red or green?
(b) What fraction of the bag of sweets is neither red nor green?

7 A bag of flour weighs $1\frac{1}{2}$ kg. Ted uses $\frac{3}{8}$ kg of flour to make some bread. How much flour will be left?

8 A carpenter buys $2\frac{3}{4}$ yards of wood. He uses $\frac{5}{8}$ yards for a job. How many yards of wood does he have left?

9 Alex watches 3 programmes on television. The programmes are:

EastEnders $\frac{1}{2}$ h

Film $1\frac{3}{4}$ h

Newsnight $\frac{3}{4}$ h

How long does Alex spend watching the 3 programmes?

10 A video tape will record up to $4\frac{3}{4}$ h of programmes. Malcolm records a film that is $2\frac{1}{2}$ h long. How much tape is left?

1.2 Dividing fractions by an integer

Teaching reference:
(*pp 68–69, section 4.11*)
pp 81–82, section 4.11

■ **To divide a fraction by an integer, multiply the fraction by the inverse of the integer.**

Example 8

Work out:

(a) $\frac{2}{7} \div 5$

(b) $\frac{6}{7} \div 3$

(c) $1\frac{3}{4} \div 5$

An integer is a whole number. To find the inverse of an integer, turn it upside down, e.g. the inverse of 5 is $\frac{1}{5}$.

(a) $\frac{2}{7} \div 5$ (Invert 5 and multiply.)

$\frac{2}{7} \times \frac{1}{5} = \frac{2 \times 1}{7 \times 5} = \frac{2}{35}$

(b) $\frac{6}{7} \div 3$ (Inverse of $3 = \frac{1}{3}$)

$\frac{6}{7} \times \frac{1}{3} = \frac{6}{21}$ (Simplify the answer.)

$\qquad\quad = \frac{2}{7}$

(c) $1\frac{3}{4} \div 5$ (Change the mixed number into an improper fraction.)

$= \frac{7}{4} \div 5$ (Invert the 5 and multiply.)

$= \frac{7}{4} \times \frac{1}{5}$

$= \frac{7}{20}$

Exercise 1B   Links (*4K*) 4K

1   Work out:

    (a) $\frac{3}{5} \div 3$ (b) $\frac{4}{7} \div 2$

    (c) $\frac{5}{8} \div 2$ (d) $\frac{3}{7} \div 6$

    (e) $\frac{3}{4} \div 5$ (f) $\frac{4}{5} \div 3$

    (g) $\frac{7}{12} \div 8$ (h) $\frac{9}{10} \div 4$

    (i) $\frac{4}{9} \div 12$ (j) $\frac{1}{2} \div 7$

2   After a party $\frac{3}{4}$ of a cake is left. This is shared by 5 people. How much does each person get?

3   $1\frac{1}{2}$ kg of flour will make 6 cakes. How much flour is needed for 1 cake?

4   A $1\frac{1}{4}$ hour film is shown in 5 equal parts. How long is each part?

5   A piece of wood measures $3\frac{1}{8}$ yards. It is cut into 5 equal lengths. How long is each length?

1.3 Working with fractions efficiently

■ **You can cancel fractions to make multiplication and division of fractions easier.**

Example 9

Work out:

(a) $\frac{3}{4} \times \frac{9}{15}$

(b) $\frac{5}{18} \times \frac{4}{15}$

(c) $\frac{6}{7} \div 3$

(a) $\frac{③ \div 3}{4} \times \frac{9}{⑮ \div 3}$ (Look for any number in the numerator that will cancel with any number in the denominator.)

$\frac{1}{4} \times \frac{9}{5} = \frac{1 \times 9}{4 \times 5}$

$= \frac{9}{20}$

(b) $\frac{⑤ \div 5}{⑱ \div 2} \times \frac{④ \div 2}{⑮ \div 5}$

$= \frac{1}{9} \times \frac{2}{3}$

$= \frac{2}{27}$

(c) $\frac{6}{7} \div 3$

$\frac{⑥ \div 3}{7} \times \frac{1}{③ \div 3}$ (Only cancel after inverting the whole number.)

$= \frac{2}{7} \times \frac{1}{1}$

$= \frac{2}{7}$

> Cancelling fractions is covered in chapter 2 of the Stage 1 Foundation book.

Exercise 1C

Look for numbers to cancel as you do this exercise.

1 $\frac{1}{2} \times \frac{4}{5}$

2 $\frac{3}{4} \times \frac{8}{15}$

3 $\frac{2}{5} \times \frac{5}{8}$

4 $\frac{1}{7} \times \frac{21}{25}$

5 $\frac{2}{3} \times \frac{9}{14}$

6 $\frac{3}{4} \times \frac{12}{21}$

7 $\frac{3}{5} \times \frac{20}{27}$

8 $\frac{4}{7} \times \frac{21}{24}$

9 $\frac{8}{15} \div 4$

10 $\frac{6}{11} \div 3$

11 $\frac{14}{25} \div 7$

12 $\frac{15}{19} \div 5$

Exercise 1D   Mixed questions

1 (a) $\frac{3}{7} + \frac{2}{7}$ (b) $\frac{7}{11} - \frac{4}{11}$ (c) $\frac{5}{8} + \frac{7}{8}$ (d) $\frac{8}{15} - \frac{3}{15}$

2 (a) $\frac{4}{5} + \frac{2}{3}$ (b) $\frac{3}{4} - \frac{2}{5}$ (c) $\frac{5}{8} - \frac{1}{4}$ (d) $\frac{7}{10} + \frac{2}{5}$

3 (a) $2\frac{1}{4} + 3\frac{3}{8}$ (b) $5\frac{3}{4} - 2\frac{1}{5}$ (c) $1\frac{4}{5} + 2\frac{1}{10}$ (d) $3\frac{5}{6} - 1\frac{3}{5}$

4 Mrs Hughes bought $2\frac{1}{4}$ kg of potatoes and $1\frac{1}{2}$ kg of carrots.
    Work out the total weight of vegetables Mrs Hughes bought.

5 A length of material measures $1\frac{7}{8}$ yards. $\frac{3}{4}$ yard is used to make
    a skirt. How much material is left?

6 Work out:
    (a) $\frac{2}{3} \div 3$ (b) $\frac{4}{5} \div 2$ (c) $\frac{7}{8} \div 4$ (d) $\frac{8}{15} \div 4$

7 $\frac{5}{8}$ of a cake is shared equally between 3 people.
    What fraction of the cake does each person receive?

8 Work out:
    (a) $\frac{3}{4} \times \frac{2}{3}$ (b) $\frac{4}{5} \times \frac{15}{18}$ (c) $\frac{1}{6} \times \frac{15}{24}$ (d) $\frac{9}{15} \times \frac{5}{6}$

Summary of key points

- To add or subtract fractions with the same denominator (bottom), add or subtract the numerators (tops) and write the answer over the denominator.

- To add or subtract fractions that have different denominators (bottoms), first find equivalent fractions that have the same denominator.

- To add or subtract mixed numbers, first add or subtract the whole numbers then add or subtract the fractions.

- To divide a fraction by an integer, multiply the fraction by the inverse of the integer.

- You can cancel fractions to make multiplication and division of fractions easier.

2 Estimating and percentage problems

2.1 Rounding to 1 significant figure

Teaching reference:
(*pp 12–16, section 1.5*)
pp 14–19, section 1.5

- The first significant figure is the first non-zero digit in a number, counting from the left.
- To write a number to 1 significant figure (1 s.f.), look at the place value of the first significant figure and round the number to this place value.

Example 1

Round the following numbers to 1 significant figure:

Rounding numbers is covered in chapter 1 of the Stage 1 Foundation book.

(a) 325 (b) 5720 (c) 8.3 (d) 0.028

(a) 325
  ↑
  3 is the 1st significant figure; it is in the hundreds column, so round this number to the nearest hundred.
  325 to 1 s.f. is 300.

(b) 5720
  ↑
  5 is the 1st s.f.; it is in the thousands column, so round to the nearest 1000.
  5720 to 1 s.f. is 6000.

(c) 8.3
  ↑
  8 is the 1st s.f.; it is in the units column, so round to the nearest whole number.
  8.3 to 1 s.f. is 8.

(d) 0.028
   ↑
  2 is the 1st s.f.; it is in the hundredths column, so round to the nearest $\frac{1}{100}$.
  0.028 to 1 s.f. $= 0.03$.

Exercise 2A   **Links (*11*) 1J**

1 Write each number correct to the nearest multiple of ten given in the brackets:

   (a) 27 (10)   (b) 328 (10)   (c) 482 (100)
   (d) 2771 (100)   (e) 3256 (1000)   (f) 4789 (1000)
   (g) 5821 (10)   (h) 476 (100)

In questions **2–4** round the numbers to 1 s.f.

2   (a) 326   (b) 4821   (c) 301   (d) 42
        (e) 5231   (f) 69 231   (g) 28   (h) 30 021

3   (a) 4.9   (b) 2.1   (c) 8.38   (d) 6.701
        (e) 9.31   (f) 9.87   (g) 2.01   (h) 3.07

4   (a) 0.34   (b) 0.69   (c) 0.081   (d) 0.0632
        (e) 0.003 21   (f) 0.0025   (g) 0.0802   (h) 0.961

5   The number of pupils in Shefford High School is 1487.
        Write this number to 1 s.f.

6   The number of spectators at a football match is 34 682.
        Write this number to 1 s.f.

7   Ted is paid a salary of £19 800.
        Write down Ted's salary to 1 s.f.

2.2 Using significant figures to estimate answers

■   **To find estimates to answers round all numbers to 1 significant figure and do the simpler calculation.**

> You can use estimated answers to check that an answer to a question is about the right size.

Example 2

For each of the following calculations write down a sum that can be used to estimate an answer, and work out the value of your estimate.

(a) $\dfrac{27 \times 321}{9.2}$ (b) 9.2×0.73

(a) $\dfrac{27 \times 321}{9.2}$

Write all the numbers in the question to 1 s.f.:

$$\frac{30 \times 300}{9}$$

then work out the estimate:

$$\frac{30 \times 300}{9} \doteq \frac{9000}{9} = 1000$$

(b) 9.2×0.73

Writing the numbers in the question to 1 s.f. gives

$$9 \times 0.7 = 6.3$$

Example 3

For each calculation:
(i) work out the exact value by calculator,
(ii) rough check your answer by estimating.

(a) 482×0.92 (b) $\dfrac{285 \times 79}{586}$

(a) 482×0.92

    (i) Using a calculator the answer is 443.44.

    (ii) An estimate would be $500 \times 0.9 = 450$.

(b) $\dfrac{285 \times 79}{586}$

    (i) Using a calculator the answer is 38.421 501 71.

    (ii) An estimate would be $\dfrac{300 \times 80}{600} = 40$.

Exercise 2B   **Links (11) 1J**

1 For each of the following calculations:

    (i) write down a calculation that can be used to work out an estimated answer,

    (ii) work out the estimated answer.

    (a) 382×43 **(b)** $962 \div 39$ **(c)** $\dfrac{823 \times 4872}{3261}$

    (d) 634×2.7 **(e)** $382 \div 4.9$ **(f)** 6.9×2.1

    (g) $8.7 \div 1.9$ **(h)** $\dfrac{3.6 \times 4.5}{9.8}$ **(i)** $\dfrac{2.4 \times 7.9}{3.9 \times 2.3}$

2 For each of the following calculations:

    (i) use your calculator to work out the exact value,

    (ii) check your answer by estimating.

    (a) 683×23 **(b)** 47×2.7 **(c)** 3.1×9.4

    (d) $385 \div 35$ **(e)** $335.4 \div 8.6$ **(f)** $9.6 \div 3.2$

    (g) $\dfrac{912 \div 24}{4.9}$ **(h)** $\dfrac{2.8 \times 3.1}{24}$

2.3 Choosing a sensible answer

There are times when you have to choose an answer that is appropriate to the question.

Example 4

Electricity bills are charged at 8.66p per unit. Mrs Bennett uses 136 units. Work out the cost of the electricity she uses.

Mrs Bennett uses 136 units that cost 8.66p each.

    So the total cost $= 136 \times 8.66\text{p}$

                   $= 1177.76\text{p}$

Mrs Bennett cannot pay 0.76p, so you should give the answer to
the nearest penny.
Mrs Bennett will pay 1178p or £11.78.

Example 5
221 people are going on a coach trip. A coach will take 52
passengers. Work out the number of coaches needed for the trip.

The number of coaches needed can be worked out by

$$\frac{221}{52} = 4.25$$

You can't hire 0.25 of a coach!
If only 4 coaches were hired they would take $4 \times 52 = 208$
passengers, so 13 people wouldn't be able to go on the trip.
Therefore 5 coaches will have to be hired.

Example 6
Malcolm is asked to draw a square that has an area of 50 cm.
He calculates that each side should be 7.071 cm.
Explain why his figure is not sensible, and give a more sensible figure.

7.071 cm is 7 cm and 0.71 mm.
You could not measure 0.71 mm.
An answer of 7.1 cm would be more sensible, as you could actually
measure this distance.

Exercise 2C   Links (*II*) 1J

Remember to check that each answer in this exercise is sensible.

1   An electricity company charges 7.44p per unit of electricity.
    Work out the cost of 176 units of electricity.

2   Mr Cumming is ordering homework books for Year 11.
    Homework books come in packs of 10. There are 143 pupils in
    Year 11. Work out the number of packs of homework books
    Mr Cumming needs to order.

3   A farmer collects 50 eggs from his chickens. How many egg
    boxes will he need if each box holds 6 eggs?

4   Mr Lowry gives his 6 grandchildren £40 to share between
    them. How much will each grandchild receive?

5   Gas costs £0.018 per kW h. Sasha uses 312 kW h.
    Calculate the cost of Sasha's gas bill.

6   A kilogram of bread dough is divided into 2 dozen bread rolls.
    Work out the weight of each bread roll.

Remember: 1 kg = 1000 g,
1 dozen = 12.

7 Dominic is asked to draw a circle with a circumference of 30 cm. He calculates that the diameter should be 9.554 cm. Explain why his answer is not sensible. Give a more sensible answer.

8 Mary carries out a survey of shoe sizes in her class. She says the average size is 4.3. Explain why this is not a sensible answer.

9 The car deck of a ferry is 30 m long. How many cars 1.8 m long can be carried on the ferry?

10 Mr Jewitt earns £4 an hour. He is paid overtime at time and a third. Mr Jewitt works 4 hours overtime and makes a request for £21.333 33 overtime payment. Explain why Mr Jewitt's request is not sensible.

2.4 Percentages in real-life situations

Percentages are used in many real-life situations, especially those involving money.

> Working out percentages is covered in chapter 3 of the Stage 1 Foundation book.

Example 7

Flash trainers

£20 + VAT
(VAT = 17.5%)

Streak trainers
Normal price: £30 *inc. VAT*
SALE PRICE:
15% reduction

(a) Work out the cost, including VAT, of Flash trainers.
(b) Work out the sale price of Streak trainers.
(c) Which pair of trainers is the cheaper?

(a) The cost of Flash trainers is

£20 + 17.5% of £20

Work out 17.5% of £20: $\dfrac{17.5}{100} \times £20 = £3.50$

Total cost of Flash trainers = £20 + £3.50
= £23.50

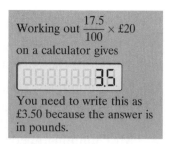

Working out $\dfrac{17.5}{100} \times £20$ on a calculator gives

```
8888888 3.5
```

You need to write this as £3.50 because the answer is in pounds.

(b) The sale price of Streak trainers is

£30 − 15% of £30
Work out 15% of £30:

$\dfrac{15}{100} \times £30 = £4.50$

Sale price of Streak trainers = £30 − £4.50
= £25.50

(c) Flash trainers are cheaper by £2.

Example 8

Peter earns a salary of £18 900. He is given a pay rise that is in line with the annual rate of inflation.
The annual rate of inflation is 2.4%.

(a) Work out the value of Peter's pay rise.
(b) Work out Peter's new salary.

(a) The pay rise is 2.4% of £18 900.

$$\frac{2.4}{100} \times £18\,900 = £453.60$$

(b) Peter's new salary is

£18 900 + £453.60
= 19 353.60

Exercise 2D   Links (*14E*) 14F

1 Work out:
   (a) 15% of £200   **(b)** 20% of £28.50
   (c) 17.5% of £35   **(d)** $33\frac{1}{3}$% of £90
   (e) 40% of £19 800   **(f)** 25% of £18.50

2 Lucy earns £15 600. She is given a pay rise of 5%.
   (a) Work out the value of Lucy's pay rise.
   (b) Work out Lucy's new salary.

3 Karen buys a new car for £18 000. After 1 year the value of the car has depreciated by 7%. Calculate the value of Karen's car after 1 year.

> 'Depreciation' means that the value is reduced.

4 Addison's department store has a winter sale. In their winter sale items in the furniture department are reduced by 30%.

Calculate the sale price of each item.

5 VAT is charged at a rate of 17.5%.
   How much VAT is there to pay on:
   (a) a garage bill of £95.50
   (b) a necklace costing £17.95
   (c) a car costing £7850?

6 Asif buys a DVD player for £375. After 1 year its value has depreciated by 45%.
   Calculate the value of Asif's DVD player after 1 year.

7 A bank charges 2% commission for changing currency. How much commission would the bank charge for changing €400?

8 Pensions are increased by the annual rate of inflation every year. In a particular year the annual rate of inflation is 1.8%.
  (a) Calculate the increase for a pension of £51.50.
  (b) Work out the new amount of the pension.

9 A holiday company offers a discount of 30% on any holidays booked before January 31st. Work out the discount on a holiday to Spain costing £379.

10 Jessica earns a salary of £24 000.
  She does not have to pay tax on the first £4560.
  She must pay 10% tax on the next £1880. She pays tax at a rate of 22% on the rest.
  (a) Calculate the amount of salary she must pay tax on.
  (b) Work out 10% of £1880.
  (c) On how much salary does she have to pay tax at a rate of 22%?
  (d) Calculate Jessica's total tax bill.

Exercise 2E   Mixed questions

1 Round the following numbers to 1 s.f.:
  (a) 32   **(b)** 45   **(c)** 237
  (d) 5800   **(e)** 3.7   **(f)** 0.02

2 23 970 people attended a pop concert. Write this number to 1 significant figure.

3 For each of the following calculations:
  (i) write down a calculation that can be used to work out an estimate of the answer,
  (ii) work out the estimated answer.

  (a) 372×54 **(b)** $\dfrac{234 \div 39}{4.9}$ **(c)** $\dfrac{3.7 \times 8.2}{7.9 \div 2.1}$

4 For each of the following calculations:
  (i) use your calculator to work out an exact answer,
  (ii) check your answer by estimating:

  (a) 587×28 **(b)** 3.2×7.8

  (c) $8.2 \div 1.7$ **(d)** $\dfrac{56 \times 38}{27}$

5 Mr Heath uses 174 units of gas. Gas costs 9.78p per unit. Work out the cost of the gas used by Mr Heath. Give your answer to a sensible degree of accuracy.

6 Cakes are sold in packs of 4. Susan wants to give 1 cake to everybody at her party. There are 17 people at the party. How many packs of cakes should Susan buy?

7 Terry is asked to draw an equilateral triangle with a perimeter of 20 cm. He works out that the length of each side of the triangle should be 6.6666 cm. Explain why his answer is not sensible. Give a more sensible answer.

8 VAT is charged at a rate of 17.5%.
Calculate the cost of the following items including VAT:
(**a**) a dressmaker's bill of £25
(**b**) a pair of trainers costing £49.99
(**c**) a new car costing £8760.

9 Be-Bop Fashions holds a summer sale. All items are reduced by $33\frac{1}{3}$%.
Calculate the sale price of the following items:

Skirt: £18.60

Dress: £60

Suit: £99.99

10 A holiday rep is paid 15% commission on any activities she sells. Calculate the commission that she earns on the following:
(**a**) boat trip €30
(**b**) beach party €25
(**c**) flamenco night €16.50.

Summary of key points

■ The first significant figure is the first non-zero digit in a number, counting from the left.

■ To write a number to 1 significant figure (1 s.f.), look at the place value of the first significant figure and round the number to this place value.

■ To find estimates to answers round all numbers to 1 significant figure and do the simpler calculation.

3 Ratio and trial and improvement

3.1 Dividing quantities in a given ratio

■ **Ratios can be used to share or divide quantities.**

Teaching reference:
(*pp 211–213, section 17.2*)
pp 264–266, section 17.2

Example 1

Mark and Joe share £25 in the ratio $2:3$.
How much does each person get?

The total number of shares is $2 + 3 = 5$.

Each share is worth $\dfrac{£25}{5} = £5$.

Mark gets $2 \times £5 = £10$.
Joe gets $3 \times £5 = £15$.

Ratios are introduced in the Stage 1 Foundation book.

Exercise 3A	**Links** (*17B, 17C*) **17B, 17C**

1 Write these ratios in their simplest form:
   (a) $8:4$ (b) $25:10$ (c) $30:10$
   (d) $125:25$ (e) $5:2\frac{1}{2}$

2 A box of chocolates contains 36 plain chocolates and 9 milk chocolates. Write down the ratio of plain chocolates to milk chocolates in its simplest form.

3 The ratio of fat to flour for pastry is $1:2$. A baker makes some pastry using 150 g fat. How much flour should the baker use?

4 Divide the following quantities in the ratio given:
   (a) £30 in the ratio $2:1$ (b) 50 cm in the ratio $2:3$
   (c) 400 g in the ratio $5:3$ (d) £10 in the ratio $3:5$
   (e) £12.50 in the ratio $3:2$.

5 The ratio of boys to girls in a class is $4:3$.
   The total number of pupils in the class is 35.
   (a) How many boys are there in the class?
   (b) How many girls are there in the class?

6 In an office the ratio of managers to other workers is $1:10$.
   A total of 55 people work in the office.
   (a) How many managers work in the office?
   (b) How many other people work in the office?

7   Louisa and Maria are given £60 by their grandfather to share in the ratio of their ages. Louisa is 5 years old and Maria is 7 years old. Work out how much each child receives.

8   A company makes a profit of £1100. The owners share the profits in the ratio 3:8. How much does each owner receive?

9   A particular shade of green paint is made by mixing blue and yellow paint in the ratio 5:3.
Work out the amounts of blue and yellow paint needed to make 5 litres of green paint.

10   Nick and Shawn share the £6 they receive for washing a car in the ratio 3:2. Work out how much each boy receives.

3.2 Solving ratio and proportion problems by the unitary method

Using the 'unitary method', you solve ratio problems by finding the value of **one unit** of the quantity.

Example 2
Penny sells 6 mince pies for £2.40. How much would she sell 8 mince pies for?

6 mince pies sell for £2.40 (240p).

1 mince pie sells for $\dfrac{240}{6}$. ———————————— Cost of 1 mince pie.

8 mince pies sell for $\dfrac{240}{6} \times 8$. ———————— 8 mince pies sell for 8 times the price of 1 mince pie.

8 mince pies sell for 320p or £3.20.

Example 3
8 roses are sold for £5. How many roses can be bought for £12.50?

£5 buys 8 roses.

£1 buys $\dfrac{8}{5}$ roses.

£12.50 buys $\dfrac{8}{5} \times 12.5 = 20$ roses.

Exercise 3B	Links (*17D*) 17D

1   5 cinema tickets cost £25. What would 8 cinema tickets cost?

2   10 CDs cost £89. How much would 7 similar CDs cost?

3   7 pencils cost 56p. How much would 15 pencils cost?

4 Janet buys 3 bottles of shampoo for £3.90. How much would 5 bottles cost?

5 Norman is paid £29.75 for 7 hours' gardening.
Work out how much he would be paid for 4 hours.

6 A list of ingredients for making scones is shown below:

> Scones: makes 12
> 250 g   flour
> 100 g   margarine
> 50 g   sugar
> 100 ml   milk

Work out the amount of each needed to make 30 scones.

7 6 magazines can be bought for £9. How many could be bought for £15?

8 4 CDs can be bought for £50. How many can be bought for £75?

9 8 pens cost 96p. How many could be bought for £1.20?

10 Jeremy bought 10 bottles of fizzy drink for £7.50. How many could be bought for £10.50?

3.3 Using trial and improvement to solve problems

Sometimes you will be asked to solve problems where there is no particular method for finding the answer. In these situations you may have to use trial and improvement.

Example 4

A group of people go to the cinema. The group pay a total of £25 for their tickets. Adult tickets cost £8 and children's tickets cost £3. How many adults and children were in the group?

1   First check that the group is not just all adults or all children.

$$\frac{£25}{£3} = 8 \text{ remainder 1; the group is not made up only of children.}$$

with £25 labelled *Total cost* and £3 labelled *Cost of 1 child*

$$\frac{£25}{£8} = 3 \text{ remainder 1; the group is not made up only of adults.}$$

with £25 labelled *Total cost* and £8 labelled *Cost of 1 adult*

2   Assume there is only 1 adult in the group:
1 adult pays £8.

$$£25 - £8 = £17$$

Check whether £17 could be just children's tickets:

$$\frac{£17}{£3} = 5 \text{ remainder 2. – NO.}$$

3 Try 2 adults:
2 adult tickets cost £16.

$$£25 - £16 = £9$$

Check whether £9 could be just children's tickets:

$$\frac{£9}{£3} = 3. - \text{YES}.$$

The group is made up of 2 adults and 3 children.

Example 5

A rectangle has an area of 32 cm². The longest side is twice the
length of the shortest side. Find the perimeter of the rectangle.

The area of a rectangle is length × breadth.
You need to find 2 numbers that multiplied together equal 32,
where one of the numbers is twice the other number.

$32 = 1 \times 32$ Is one number twice the other? – **NO.**
$32 = 2 \times 16$ Is one number twice the other? – **NO.**
$32 = 4 \times 8$ Is one number twice the other? – **YES.**

The two sides are 4 cm and 8 cm.

The perimeter is $2 \times (\text{length} + \text{breadth})$

$$= 2 \times (4 + 8)$$
$$= 2 \times 12^\sim$$
$$= 24 \text{ cm}$$

Exercise 3C

1 A group of friends visit a sports centre. Some of the group go
swimming and the rest play squash. Tickets for swimming cost
£3 and tickets for squash cost £5. The total cost of their tickets
is £22. Work out how many of the group went swimming and
how many played squash.

2 Pens cost 15p and pencils cost 8p. Mary bought a mixture of
pens and pencils for 70p. How many of each did she buy?

3 A rectangle has an area of 54 cm². One of its sides is 6 times
longer than the other. Calculate the perimeter of the
rectangle.

4 Three different isosceles triangles each have a perimeter of 11 cm.
The sides of the triangles are whole numbers of centimetres long.
Write down the lengths of the sides of the isosceles triangles.

> Check that your answer
> will make triangles.

5 Draw a rectangle whose area is numerically equal to its
perimeter.

6   A football team plays 4 matches during Christmas.
They win a total of 7 points. If they score 3 points for a win, 1
point for a draw and no points for a defeat, how many games
did they win, draw and lose?

7   Two moons, Zeus and Hermes, orbit the same planet.
Zeus takes 24 days to orbit the planet and Hermes takes
32 days. If the two moons start in line with each other, how
long will it be before they line up again?

8   A restaurant charges 40p for coffee and 35p for tea. Miss
Hone buys coffee and tea for her friends. She pays £3 for the
drinks. How many cups of tea and coffee does she buy?

Exercise 3D   **Mixed questions**

1   A box of chocolates contains 18 plain chocolates and 9 milk
chocolates. Write down the ratio of plain chocolates to milk
chocolates in its simplest form.

2   Divide the following quantities in the ratio given:
(a) £40 in the ratio $3:2$
(b) 80 cm in the ratio $5:3$
(c) £16 in the ratio $1:4$.

3   John and Kevin are given £150 to share in the ratio of their ages.
John is 8 and Kevin is 7. How much does each boy receive?

4   The ratio of boys to girls in a class is $3:2$. There are 25 pupils
in the class. How many girls are there?

5   William and Mary share £7 in the ratio $1:3$. How much does
each of them receive?

6   Eric buys 5 packets of biscuits for £3. How much would 8
packets of the same biscuits cost?

7   Karen is paid £42.40 for working 8 hours in a burger bar. How
much would Karen be paid for working 11 hours at the same
rate?

8   A gardener is paid £25 for 4 hours' work. How long would he
have to work to earn £43.75?

9   In a cafe, biscuits cost 15p and cakes cost 25p. Robert bought
a mixture of biscuits and cakes for £1.10. How many biscuits
and cakes did Robert buy?

10 A rectangle has an area of 36 cm². One of its sides is 4 times
the length of the other. Work out the lengths of the sides of
the rectangle.

Summary of key points

- **Ratios can be used to share or divide quantities.**

4 Decimals and decimal calculations

4.1 Rounding decimal numbers

■ **To round a decimal correct to one place of decimals (1 d.p.) you look at the second place of decimals. If it is 5 or more you round up; if it is less you leave this and any remaining numbers out.**

To correct to two places of decimals you look at the third place.
To correct to three places you look at the fourth place, and so on.

Example 1

Round the following numbers correct to

(i)   one decimal place

(ii) two decimal places:

(a) 35.384

(b) 46.955

(a) (i)   35.384 = 35.4 to 1 d.p.

8 is more than 5
so round the
3 to 4.

(ii) 35.384 = 35.38 to 2 d.p.

4 is less than
5 so leave this
and any other
numbers out.

(b) (i)   46.955 = 47.0 to 1 d.p.

As this is 5,
round the 9
to 10, and the
6 to 7 from the
carry from 10.

(ii) 46.955 = 46.96 to 2 d.p.

As this is 5,
round the 5
to 6.

Exercise 4A   **Links (*6B*) 6C**

1   Round these numbers to one place of decimals:
   - **(a)** 8.34
   - **(b)** 3.564
   - **(c)** 0.391
   - **(d)** 15.145
   - **(e)** 7.952
   - **(f)** 4.99
   - **(g)** 1000.09
   - **(h)** 0.555
   - **(i)** 50.05

2   Round these numbers to two places of decimals:
   - **(a)** 10.059
   - **(b)** 8.445
   - **(c)** 0.0145
   - **(d)** 99.999
   - **(e)** 0.0176
   - **(f)** 17.499
   - **(g)** 29.4631
   - **(h)** 0.057
   - **(i)** 2.4539

4.2 Multiplying decimals

■   **When multiplying decimals, the answer must have the same number of decimal places as the total number of decimal places in the numbers being multiplied.**

Example 2

Work out the cost of 16 CDs at £8.45 each.
Do not use a calculator.

```
  8 4 5        These are
  ×1 6         the carries.     Multiply the numbers together,
 ─────────                      ignoring the decimals.
  5 0²7³0  ── 845 × 6
  8 4 5 0  ── 845 × 10    (Remember the 0 as you are multiplying by ten.)
 ─────────
 1 3 5 2 0  ── Add them together.
        1
```

> This is sometimes called long multiplication.

Count the number of decimal places: 16×8.45: 2 places.

So $16 \times £8.45 = £135.20$.

Example 3

Work out 6.3×5.4 using equivalent fractions.
Do not use a calculator.

$$6.3 = \frac{63}{10}$$

$$5.4 = \frac{54}{10}$$

So

$$6.3 \times 5.4 = \frac{63}{10} \times \frac{54}{10}$$

$$= \frac{63 \times 54}{10 \times 10}$$

$$= \frac{3402}{100}$$

$$= 34.02$$

> Work out 63×54 by long multiplication:
>
> ```
>       6 3
>     × 5 4
>   ─────────
>     2 5¹2
>   3 1¹5 0
>   ─────────
>   3 4 0 2
> ```

Exercise 4B   Links (*6F, 6G*)

Work these out without using a calculator, showing all your working.

1   Work out the cost of:
    (a) 8 paperbacks at £5.45 each
    (b) 5 boxes of crackers at £8.19 each
    (c) 26 bottles of oil at £2.36 each
    (d) 3.5 kg of potatoes at £0.46 per kg
    (e) 14 pairs of socks at £3.89 a pair.

2   Use the method of equivalent fractions to work out:
    (a) 0.4×0.7 **(b)** 0.8×0.6 **(c)** 3.2×1.4
    (d) 8.5×6.7 **(e)** 9.1×4.5 **(f)** 4.1×0.6

3   Work out the total length, in metres, of fourteen pieces of wood if each is 1.27 metres long.

4   Calculate the total cost of 5 bottles of lemonade which cost 98p each and 9 packets of crisps which cost £1.29 each.

5   Work out:
    (a) 17.2×5.4 **(b)** 25.9×6.8 **(c)** 51.2×2.7

Example 4
Change the following times into fractions and decimal fractions:

(a) 2 hours 15 minutes
(b) 3 hours 30 minutes
(c) 1 hour 35 minutes.

(a) 2 hours 15 minutes

$$= 2\tfrac{15}{60} = 2\tfrac{1}{4} \text{ hours}$$

As a decimal fraction $= 2.25$ hours.

(b) 3 hours 30 minutes

$$= 3\tfrac{30}{60} = 3\tfrac{1}{2} \text{ hours}$$

As a decimal fraction $= 3.5$ hours.

(c) 1 hour 35 minutes

$$= 1\tfrac{35}{60} = 1\tfrac{7}{12} \text{ hours}$$

As a decimal fraction $= 1.58$ hours to 2 d.p.

> Remember: there are 60 minutes in one hour.

> You may use your calculator for this:
>
>  $= 2.25$

Example 5

A fairground charges £2.40 for 10 minutes
on a go-kart.
What is the charge for 1 hour?

$$10 \text{ minutes} = \frac{10}{60} \text{ of one hour}$$

$$= \frac{1}{6}$$

Keep $\frac{1}{6}$; do not round to a decimal as your answer will not be accurate.

so   no. of 10 minute sessions in 1 hour $= 1 \div \frac{1}{6}$

$$= 6 \text{ sessions}$$

So charge $= £2.40 \times 6$

$$= £14.40$$

If you use your calculator, 2.40×6 gives £14.4. Remember you need two d.p. to show the number of pence, so put in the zero.

1   Change the following times into

    (i) fractions   **(ii)** decimal fractions.

    (a) 1 hour 15 minutes   **(b)** 3 hours 45 minutes
    (c) 4 hours 30 minutes   **(d)** 2 hours 20 minutes
    (e) 3 hours 55 minutes   **(f)** 6 hours 10 minutes.

2   A strawberry picker can pick a box of strawberries in
20 minutes.
She is paid £1.80 to pick them.
    (a) How many boxes can she pick in 2 hours?
    (b) How much will she be paid?

3   A train travels 10 miles in 6 minutes.
How long will it take to travel 125 miles?
Give your answer in hours and fractions of an hour.

Summary of key points

■ **To round a decimal correct to one place of decimals (1 d.p.)
you look at the second place of decimals. If it is 5 or more
you round up; if it is less you leave this and any remaining
numbers out.**

■ **When multiplying decimals, the answer must have the
same number of decimal places as the total number of
decimal places in the numbers being multiplied.**

5 Rules of algebra 1

5.1 Expanding brackets

■ **When you expand brackets you multiply *every* term inside the brackets by the term outside.**

Example 1

Expand the brackets in these expressions:

(a) $5(x + y)$

(b) $c(c - 3)$

(a) $5(x + y) = 5 \times x + 5 \times y$
$$= 5x + 5y$$

(b) $c(c - 3) = c \times c - 3 \times c$
$$= c^2 - 3c$$

With practice, you should be able to write the answer straight down without the working.

Exercise 5A 　　　　　　　　　　　　　**Links (2I) 2I**

Expand the brackets in these expressions.

1	$3(p + q)$	**2**	$6(a - b)$	**3**	$3(x + 5)$
4	$y(y + 4)$	**5**	$c(c - 1)$	**6**	$a(2x + 3y)$
7	$n(5a - 4b)$	**8**	$t(3t + 7)$	**9**	$y(2y - 5)$
10	$c(6c + 1)$	**11**	$p(a - b)$	**12**	$x(px - q)$

5.2 Factorizing

■ **Factorizing is the reverse process to expanding brackets.**

■ **To factorize an expression, you find the common factor of the terms in the expression and write the common factor outside a bracket. Then you complete the brackets with an expression which, when multiplied by the common factor, gives the original expression. The common factor may be a number or it may be a letter.**

> For example, the common factor of $8x$ and $12y$ is 4 and the common factor of ab and ac is a.

Example 2

Factorize $5a + 15b$.

$$5a + 15b = 5(a + 3b)$$

> 5 is the common factor of $5a$ and $15b$ and so you write 5 outside the brackets.

Example 3

Factorize $8x - 12y$.

$$8x - 12y = 4(2x - 3y)$$

> 4 is the common factor of $8x$ and $12y$ and so you write 4 outside the brackets.

Example 4

Factorize $ab + ac$.

$$ab + ac = a(b + c)$$

a is the common factor of ab and ac and so you write a outside the brackets.

Example 5

Factorize $x^2 - 4x$.

$$x^2 - 4x = x(x - 4)$$

x is the common factor of x^2 and $4x$ and so you write x outside the brackets.

Exercise 5B   **Links 2P**

Factorize the following expressions.

1	$2x + 6y$	**2**	$10a - 5b$	**3**	$4p + 12$
4	$8c - 6d$	**5**	$12p + 9q$	**6**	$ax + bx$
7	$2ax - 3ay$	**8**	$15t + 5$	**9**	$y^2 + 2y$
10	$c^2 - cy$	**11**	$p^2 + 6px$	**12**	$6 - 18q$
13	$15d + 25$	**14**	$a^2 - 3a$	**15**	$7x + x^2$
16	$4p^2 - 5pq$	**17**	$2n^2 + 5n$	**18**	$5y^2 - 3y$
19	$2x - 3x^2$	**20**	$7a^2 + a$	**21**	$t - 5t^2$

5.3 Substituting numbers into expressions

■ **If you know the value of the letter or letters used in an algebraic expression, you can work out the value of the expression.**

■ **Replacing letters by numbers is called *substituting*.**

In this section, you will not have to use negative numbers.

Example 6

$a = 5$ and $b = 3$.

Work out the value of:

(a) $2a - b$ (b) $4ab$ (c) $a^2 + 4$

(a) $2a - b = 2 \times 5 - 3$
$$= 10 - 3$$
$$= 7$$

(b) $4ab = 4 \times 5 \times 3$
$$= 60$$

(c) $a^2 + 4 = 5^2 + 4$
$$= 5 \times 5 + 4$$
$$= 25 + 4$$
$$= 29$$

Example 7

$p = 2, q = 7$ and $r = 0$.

Work out the value of:

(a) $3pq + 5qr$ (b) $p(q - 1)$ (c) $5p^3$

(a) $3pq + 5qr = 3 \times 2 \times 7 + 5 \times 7 \times 0$

$\qquad\qquad = 42 + 0$ ——————————————— $35 \times 0 = 0$

$\qquad\qquad = 42$

(b) $p(q - 1) = 2 \times (7 - 1)$

$\qquad\qquad = 2 \times 6$

$\qquad\qquad = 12$

(c) $5p^3 = 5 \times 2^3$

$\qquad = 5 \times 8$ ——————————————— $2^3 = 2 \times 2 \times 2 = 8$

$\qquad = 40$

Exercise 5C   **Links (*21C, 21D*) 21C, 21D**

In this exercise $p = 3, q = 2, r = 5$ and $s = 0$.

Work out the value of the following expressions.

1 $p + r$	**2** $4q$	**3** pq
4 rs	**5** $7qr$	**6** $6p + 4q$
7 $5p - 2r$	**8** $4p - 6q$	**9** $7p + 8s$
10 pqr	**11** qrs	**12** $pr + 4q$
13 $pr - pq$	**14** $qr - pq$	**15** $qr + rs$
16 $6pq + 3qr$	**17** $4qr - 5pq$	**18** $6pr - 7qs$
19 $4(p + 7)$	**20** $6(r - 2)$	**21** $5(p + q)$
22 $p(q + 4)$	**23** $r(r - 2)$	**24** $q(p + r)$
25 $p(r - q)$	**26** p^2	**27** $5p^2$
28 $r^2 + 1$	**29** $3r^2 - 2$	**30** $5q^2 + 7$
31 $(q + 1)^2$	**32** $(r - 4)^2$	**33** r^3
34 $2p^3$	**35** $6q^3$	**36** $p^2 + r^2$
37 $(p + r)^2$	**38** $(p + q)^3$	**39** $p^3 - q^3$
40 $(p - q)^3$		

5.4 Substituting negative numbers into expressions

■   **Sometimes, you will have to substitute negative numbers into algebraic expressions.**

28 Rules of algebra 1

Example 8

$p = 2, q = -3$ and $r = -5$.

Work out the value of:

(a) $p + r$ (b) $q - r$ (c) pq (d) qr
(e) $p(q + r)$ (f) $r^2 + 6r$ (g) $(p + q)^2$ (h) $4r^3$

(a) $p + r = 2 + (-5)$
$= 2 - 5$ ——————————— Adding a negative number is the same as subtracting.
$= -3$

(b) $q - r = -3 - (-5)$
$= -3 + 5$ ——————————— Subtracting a negative number is the same as adding.
$= 2$

(c) $pq = 2 \times -3$ ——————————— When you multiply two numbers which have different signs, the answer is negative. (Remember: 2 means +2.)
$= -6$

(d) $qr = -3 \times -5$ ——————————— When you multiply two numbers which have the same sign, the answer is positive.
$= 15$

(e) $p(q + r) = 2 \times (-3 + (-5))$ (f) $r^2 + 6r = (-5)^2 + 6 \times -5$
$= 2 \times (-3 - 5)$ $= (-5 \times -5) - 30$
$= 2 \times -8$ $= 25 - 30$
$= -16$ $= -5$

(g) $(p + q)^2 = (2 + (-3))^2$ (h) $4r^3 = 4 \times (-5)^3$
$= (2 - 3)^2$ $= 4 \times (-5 \times -5 \times -5)$
$= (-1)^2$ $= 4 \times -125$
$= -1 \times -1$ $= -500$
$= 1$

Exercise 5D   Links (*21G, 21I*) 21H, 21I, 21K

In this exercise $a = -5, b = 6$ and $c = -2$.

Work out the value of the following expressions.

1 $a + b$	**2** $a - b$	**3** $b - a$	**4** $a - c$
5 $b - c$	**6** $a + b + c$	**7** $3a + 7$	**8** $4a + 3b$
9 $2b + 5c$	**10** $2a - 5c$	**11** $3b - 2a$	**12** ab
13 ac	**14** $3bc$	**15** $bc - 1$	**16** $ab - bc$
17 $2ab + 3ac$	**18** $3ac - 2bc$	**19** abc	**20** $3(a + 1)$
21 $5(c - 1)$	**22** $a(b + c)$	**23** $b(c - a)$	**24** $c(a + b)$
25 a^2	**26** $3c^2$	**27** $4a^2 - 3$	**28** $5c^2 + 3c$
29 $2a^2 - 3a$	**30** $(a + 1)^2$	**31** $(c + 3)^2$	**32** $(a + b)^2$
33 $(a + c)^2$	**34** $(c - a)^2$	**35** $2b^3$	**36** $3a^3$
37 $6c^3$	**38** $2(b + c)^2$	**39** $a^2 - b^2$	**40** $(a - c)^3$

Exercise 5E   Mixed questions

1   Expand the brackets in these expressions:
    (a) $6(m + n)$ **(b)** $5(x - y)$ **(c)** $4(p - 1)$
    (d) $t(t + 1)$ **(e)** $q(q - 5)$ **(f)** $p(2p + q)$
    (g) $a(3x - 4y)$ **(h)** $c(a - bc)$

2   Factorize:
    (a) $5x + 15y$ **(b)** $15p - 9q$ **(c)** $cd + ce$
    (d) $x^2 - 7x$ **(e)** $t^2 + at$ **(f)** $bx^2 - x$
    (g) $3p^2 + py$ **(h)** $aq^2 - at$

3 $w = 4$, $x = 7$ and $y = 0$.
    Work out the value of:
    (a) $w + x$ **(b)** $3x$ **(c)** $5xy$
    (d) $2wx$ **(e)** $3w + 2x$ **(f)** $2(w + 3)$
    (g) $4(x - 1)$ **(h)** $y(3x - w)$ **(i)** $2x^2$
    (j) $(x + 2)^2$ **(k)** w^3 **(l)** $(x - w)^3$

4 $v = 3$, $w = -2$ and $x = -4$.
    Work out the value of:
    (a) $v + w$ **(b)** $v - x$ **(c)** $w - x$
    (d) vw **(e)** wx **(f)** vwx
    (g) $2v + 5w$ **(h)** $2w - x$ **(i)** $6(v - 5)$
    (j) $3w^2$ **(k)** $w^2 + 5w$ **(l)** $2x^3$

Summary of key points

- **When you expand brackets, you multiply *every* term inside the brackets by the term outside.**

- **Factorizing is the reverse process to expanding brackets.**

- **To factorize an expression, you find the common factor of the terms in the expression and write the common factor outside a bracket. Then you complete the brackets with an expression which, when multiplied by the common factor, gives the original expression. The common factor may be a number or it may be a letter.**

  For example, the common factor of $8x$ and $12y$ is 4 and the common factor of ab and ac is a.

- **If you know the value of the letter or letters used in an algebraic expression, you can work out the value of the expression.**

- **Replacing letters by numbers is called *substituting*.**

- **Sometimes, you will have to substitute negative numbers into algebraic expressions.**

6 Rules of algebra 2

6.1 Solving equations by balancing

- In an equation, a letter represents a number.

- Solving an equation means finding which number the letter represents. This number is called the *solution* of the equation.

- To rearrange an equation you can
  - add the same quantity to each side
  - subtract the same quantity from each side
  - multiply each side by the same quantity
  - divide each side by the same quantity.

- Whatever you do to one side of an equation you must also do to the other side. This is called the **balance** method.

Example 1
Solve the equation $a + 5 = 8$.

$a = 8 - 5$ Take 5 away from each side.

$a = 3$

> -5 is the *opposite* process of $+5$.

Example 2
Solve the equation $4b = 28$.
This means $4 \times b = 28$.

$b = \dfrac{28}{4}$ Divide each side by 4.

$b = 7$

> $\div 4$ is the *opposite* process of $\times 4$.
>
> $\dfrac{28}{4}$ means $28 \div 4$.

Example 3
Solve the equation $6c - 7 = 17$.

$6c = 17 + 7$ Add 7 to each side.

$6c = 24$

$c = \dfrac{24}{6}$ Divide each side by 6.

$c = 4$

- The solution of an equation is not always a whole number. It can, for example, be a fraction or a decimal.

Example 4
Solve the equation $5d + 1 = 3$.

$5d = 3 - 1$ Take 1 away from each side.
$5d = 2$
$d = \frac{2}{5}$ Divide each side by 5.

■ **You can use the balance method to solve equations with the letter on both sides. You rearrange the equation so that, on one side, there is the letter with a positive number in front of it and, on the other side, there is a number.**

Example 5
Solve the equation $7x + 2 = 5x + 11$.
Collect all the x terms on one side:

$2x + 2 = 11$ Take $5x$ away from each side.

Collect the numbers on the other side:

$2x = 9$ Take 2 away from each side.
$x = \dfrac{9}{2}$ Divide each side by 2.
$x = 4\frac{1}{2}$

> If you took $7x$ away from each side, you would not affect the balance of the equation but you would get a negative number in front of x.

Exercise 6A   **Links** (*15A–H, 15M, 15N*) **15A–H, 15M, 15N**

Solve these equations.

1	$a + 7 = 12$	**2**	$c - 4 = 6$	**3**	$3p = 21$
4	$\dfrac{d}{4} = 3$	**5**	$5x + 4 = 19$	**6**	$6b - 7 = 17$
7	$4y + 9 = 9$	**8**	$5t = 3$	**9**	$2q = 5$
10	$3n = 8$	**11**	$2r + 7 = r + 10$	**12**	$3x - 2 = x + 8$
13	$5c + 4 = 2c + 19$	**14**	$7p - 9 = 3p - 1$	**15**	$8c - 5 = 3c - 5$
16	$3b + 4 = b + 5$	**17**	$5d - 2 = 2d + 3$	**18**	$7y - 9 = 2y - 5$
19	$3t + 8 = 6t + 1$	**20**	$2w = 8w - 15$		

6.2 Equations with negative solutions

■ **The solution of an equation can be a negative number.**

Example 6
Solve the equation $3x + 10 = 4$.

$3x = 4 - 10$ Take 10 away from each side.
$3x = -6$
$x = \dfrac{-6}{3}$ Divide each side by 3.
$x = -2$

Example 7

Solve the equation $5y - 1 = 3y - 8$.

$$2y - 1 = -8 \qquad \text{Take } 3y \text{ away from each side.}$$
$$2y = -7 \qquad \text{Add 1 to each side.}$$
$$y = \frac{-7}{2} \qquad \text{Divide each side by 2.}$$
$$y = -3\tfrac{1}{2}$$

Exercise 6B   Links (*15I*) 15I

Solve these equations.

1 $a + 7 = 3$	**2** $5b = -30$	**3** $c - 2 = -3$
4 $d + 4 = -5$	**5** $2e = -11$	**6** $6f = -5$
7 $3g = -17$	**8** $3h + 7 = 1$	**9** $5k + 8 = 3$
10 $4m + 5 = 2$	**11** $5n + 9 = 1$	**12** $6p + 19 = 2$
13 $6q + 7 = 3$	**14** $3r + 5 = 2r + 1$	**15** $6t + 1 = 3t - 5$
16 $7u - 6 = 4u - 15$	**17** $9v + 7 = 3v + 2$	**18** $5w + 8 = 3w - 5$
19 $8x - 3 = 2x - 7$	**20** $3y - 5 = 7y + 5$	

All the solutions in **Exercise 6B** are negative numbers.

Exercise 6C   Links (*15J*) 15J

Solve these equations.

1 $6a + 1 = 25$	**2** $3b - 4 = 20$	**3** $4c + 9 = 5$
4 $5d - 2 = 1$	**5** $2e + 9 = 2$	**6** $8f + 3 = 9$
7 $9g - 7 = 8$	**8** $\dfrac{h}{3} = -4$	**9** $3k + 5 = 11$
10 $5m - 1 = 2$	**11** $4n + 3 = 3n + 8$	**12** $7p - 2 = 4p + 7$
13 $8q + 7 = 6q + 1$	**14** $9r - 2 = 3r + 2$	**15** $9t + 8 = 3t - 2$
16 $7u - 2 = 2u - 5$	**17** $8v + 3 = 4v + 13$	**18** $6w + 7 = 2w - 17$
19 $3x - 5 = 11x - 6$	**20** $4y - 9 = 9y + 8$	

The solutions in **Exercise 6C** are a mixture of positive numbers and negative numbers.

6.3 Equations with brackets

■ **In an equation with brackets, expand the brackets first.**

Example 8

Solve the equation $4(x + 2) = 28$.

$$4x + 8 = 28 \qquad \text{Expand the brackets.}$$
$$4x = 20 \qquad \text{Take 8 away from each side.}$$
$$x = 5 \qquad \text{Divide each side by 4.}$$

> Alternative method:
> Divide each side by 4:
> $$x + 2 = 7$$
> Subtract 2 from each side:
> $$x = 5$$

Example 9

Solve the equation $3(2y - 5) = 12$.

$$6y - 15 = 12 \qquad \text{Expand the brackets.}$$
$$6y = 27 \qquad \text{Add 15 to each side.}$$
$$y = \frac{27}{6} \qquad \text{Divide each side by 6.}$$
$$y = 4\tfrac{1}{2}$$

Exercise 6D   Links (*15K, 15L*) 15K, 15L

Solve these equations.

1	$2(a + 1) = 10$	**2**	$3(b - 2) = 15$	**3**	$4(c + 3) = 36$
4	$5(d - 6) = 20$	**5**	$2(e + 3) = 7$	**6**	$3(f + 1) = 1$
7	$3(g - 2) = 5$	**8**	$3(h + 4) = 9$	**9**	$3(2k + 1) = 9$
10	$2(4m - 3) = 18$	**11**	$5(2n + 3) = 15$	**12**	$6(3p + 2) = 48$
13	$2(4q - 1) = 4$	**14**	$3(4r + 11) = 9$	**15**	$5(4t - 3) = 35$

■ **Equations with brackets may also have the letter on both sides.**

Example 10

Solve the equation $5(x - 4) = 2x + 7$.

$$5x - 20 = 2x + 7 \qquad \text{Expand the brackets.}$$
$$3x - 20 = 7 \qquad \text{Take } 2x \text{ away from each side.}$$
$$3x = 27 \qquad \text{Add 20 to each side.}$$
$$x = 9 \qquad \text{Divide each side by 3.}$$

Example 11

Solve the equation $8(y + 6) = 3(y + 1)$.

$$8y + 48 = 3y + 3 \qquad \text{Expand the brackets.}$$
$$5y + 48 = 3 \qquad \text{Take } 3y \text{ away from each side.}$$
$$5y = -45 \qquad \text{Take 48 away from each side.}$$
$$y = -9 \qquad \text{Divide each side by 5.}$$

Exercise 6E   Links (*150*) 15O

Solve these equations.

1	$3(a + 5) = a + 21$	**2**	$5(b - 4) = 2b + 1$	**3**	$7c - 2 = 3(c + 6)$
4	$6(d - 2) = 5(d - 1)$	**5**	$8(e - 1) = 5(e + 2)$	**6**	$9(f - 2) = 2(f + 3)$
7	$7(g - 1) = 5(g - 1)$	**8**	$5(h + 3) = 3(h + 5)$	**9**	$4(2k + 5) = 3(k + 10)$
10	$4(2m + 1) = 3(5m - 1)$	**11**	$3(2n - 1) = 3n - 2$	**12**	$5(p + 2) = 2(p - 1)$
13	$5(q + 2) = 2(q - 1)$	**14**	$4(3r - 2) = 3(3r + 1)$	**15**	$2(3t - 4) = 5(2t - 1)$

6.4 Equations with negative numbers

■ **Equations may have a negative number in front of a letter.**

Example 12

Solve the equation $9 - 2x = 1$.

$9 = 2x + 1$ Add $2x$ to each side.
$8 = 2x$ Take 1 away from each side.
$x = 4$ Divide each side by 2.

> Alternative method:
> Subtract 9 from each side:
> $$-2x = -8$$
> Divide each side by -2:
> $$x = \frac{-8}{-2}$$
> $$= 4$$

Exercise 6F

Solve these equations.

1	$8 - a = 5$	**2**	$13 - 3b = 1$	**3**	$11 - 4c = 1$	**4**	$7 - d = 9$
5	$5 - 4d = 3$	**6**	$9 - 7f = 9$	**7**	$5 - 3g = 7$	**8**	$14 - 5f = 1$
9	$3 - 4k = 9$	**10**	$3 - 4m = 23$	**11**	$4 - 5n = 1$	**12**	$4 - 3p = 18$

■ **Equations may have brackets and a negative number in front of a letter.**

Example 13

Solve the equation $3(x - 1) = 4 - 5x$.

$3x - 3 = 4 - 5x$ Expand the brackets.
$8x - 3 = 4$ Add $5x$ to each side.
$8x = 7$ Add 3 to each side.
$x = \frac{7}{8}$ Divide each side by 8.

■ **Equations may have the letter on both sides and a negative number in front of a letter.**

Example 14

Solve the equation $5y + 17 = 3 - 2y$.

$7y + 17 = 3$ Add $2y$ to each side.
$7y = -14$ Take 17 away from each side.
$y = -2$ Divide each side by 7.

Exercise 6G

Solve these equations.

1 $2(a + 1) = 17 - 3a$

2 $3(b - 5) = 13 - 4b$

3 $4(2 + c) = 26 - 5c$

4 $5(d - 3) = 15 - d$

5 $2(e + 4) = 8 - 5e$

6 $7 - 2f = 3(f - 1)$

7 $4g + 1 = 29 - 3g$

8 $3h - 7 = 23 - 2h$

9 $4k + 7 = 25 - 2k$

10 $5m + 9 = 9 - 4m$

11 $3n - 13 = 15 - n$

12 $33 - 2p = 3 + 4p$

13 $2(q + 3) = 11 - 6q$

14 $3(r + 7) = 1 - 2r$

15 $5(t - 3) = 13 - 3t$

16 $6 - u = 4(2 + u)$

17 $7v + 23 = 5 - 2v$

18 $3w - 1 = 1 - 3w$

19 $2 - x = 3x + 8$

20 $3y - 14 = 8 - 5y$

Exercise 6H   Mixed questions

Solve these equations.

1 $6a - 7 = 11$

2 $4b + 9 = 1$

3 $3c - 2 = 9$

4 $8d + 1 = 3d + 11$

5 $7e - 2 = 3e + 1$

6 $f - 12 = 4f$

7 $5(g + 3) = 35$

8 $4(h + 3) = 22$

9 $3(2k + 5) = 14$

10 $7m + 1 = 3(m + 3)$

11 $6(n - 2) = 2n - 19$

12 $7(p - 2) = 2(p + 3)$

13 $3(2q + 5) = 10q + 13$

14 $3(4r - 5) = 2(7r - 3)$

15 $9 - 4t = 2$

16 $4 - 5u = 19$

17 $3(v + 2) = 13 - 4v$

18 $6(w + 2) = 12 - w$

19 $2 - 3x = 7x + 5$

20 $4y + 21 = 6 - 5y$

Summary of key points

■ **In an equation, a letter represents a number.**

■ **Solving an equation means finding which number the letter represents. This number is called the *solution* of the equation.**

■ **To rearrange an equation you can**
  ● **add the same quantity to each side**
  ● **subtract the same quantity from each side**
  ● **multiply each side by the same quantity**
  ● **divide each side by the same quantity.**

■ **Whatever you do to one side of an equation you must also do to the other side. This is called the balance method.**

■ **The solution of an equation is not always a whole number. It can, for example, be a fraction or a decimal.**

■ **You can use the balance method to solve equations with the letter on both sides. You rearrange the equation so that, on one side, there is the letter with a positive number in front of it and, on the other side, there is a number.**

■ **The solution of an equation can be a negative number.**

■ **In an equation with brackets, expand the brackets first.**

■ **You should be able to solve equations with one or more of the following:**
  ● **brackets**
  ● **the letter on both sides**
  ● **a negative number in front of the letter.**

7 Graphs and functions

7.1 Coordinates and lines parallel to the axes

Teaching reference:
pp 137–139, section 9.1

- ■ You can describe positions on a grid using coordinates.
- ■ Lines parallel to the *x*-axis have equations *y* = a constant.
- ■ Lines parallel to the *y*-axis have equations *x* = a constant.
- ■ The mid-point of the line segment joining (*a*, *b*) and (*c*, *d*) is

$$\left(\frac{a+c}{2}, \frac{b+d}{2} \right)$$

Worked examination question (modified)

(a) Write down the coordinates of:
   (i) point *A*
   (ii) point *B*.
(b) (i) On the grid, plot the point $(-2, 5)$.
      Label it point *P*.
   (ii) On the grid, plot the point $(5, 0)$.
      Label it point *Q*.
(c) Find the coordinates of the mid-point of *PQ*.
(d) Write down the equation of the line marked **L**.
(e) Write down the equation of the line marked **M**.

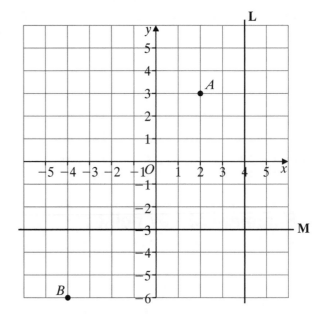

(a) (i) The coordinates of *A* are (2, 3).
   (ii) The coordinates of *B* are $(-4, -6)$.
(b) The points *P* and *Q* are shown right:
(c) $P = (-2, 5)$ $Q = (5, 0)$

   Mid-point of *PQ*:

   $$x\text{-coordinate} = \frac{-2+5}{2} = 1\tfrac{1}{2}$$

   $$y\text{-coordinate} = \frac{5+0}{2} = 2\tfrac{1}{2}$$

   So mid-point = $(1\tfrac{1}{2}, 2\tfrac{1}{2})$.

(d) Every point on the line **L** has an *x*-coordinate of 4.
   So the equation of line **L** is $x = 4$.
(e) Every point on the line **M** has a *y*-coordinate of -3.
   So the equation of line **M** is $y = -3$.

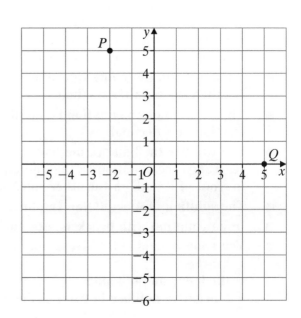

Example 1

The points A, B and C have these coordinates:

A is (1, 1), B is (4, 3) and C is (2, 6).

$ABCD$ is a square.

(a) Find the coordinates of D.

(b) Find the coordinates of the centre of the square.

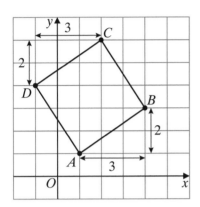

The shift from A to B is 3 right, 2 up.

So the shift from C to D must be 3 to left, 2 down.

(a) By eye, D is (−1, 4).

(b) The centre of the square is the mid-point of either diagonal, AC or BD.

A is (1, 1) C is (2, 6).

The mid-point of AC is

$$\left(\frac{1+2}{2}, \frac{1+6}{2}\right) = \left(\frac{3}{2}, \frac{7}{2}\right) \text{ or } (1\tfrac{1}{2}, 3\tfrac{1}{2})$$

Exercise 7A

1   The diagram shows a triangle ABC.
   (a) Write down the coordinates of:
      (i) point A
      (ii) point B
      (iii) point C.
   (b) $ABCD$ is a parallelogram.
      Find the coordinates of D.
   (c) Find the coordinates of the mid-point of:
      (i) AC
      (ii) CD
   (d) Write down the equation of the line AC.

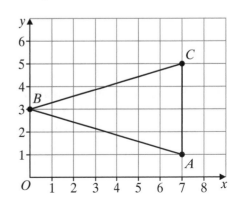

2 **(a)** On a grid draw the lines $x = 5$ and $y = -2$.
 (b) Find the coordinates of the point of intersection of the
  lines $x = 5$ and $y = -2$.

3

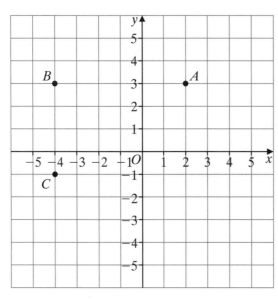

ABCD is a rectangle.
The points *A*, *B* and *C* are shown on the grid.
 (a) Write down the coordinates of:
  (i) point *A*   **(ii)** point *B*   **(iii)** point *C*.
 (b) Plot the point *D* and write down its coordinates.
 (c) Write down the equation of the line *AB*.
 (d) Find the coordinates of the centre of the rectangle *ABCD*.

7.2 Straight lines passing through the origin

Teaching reference:
pp 140–142, section 9.2

■ **The equation of the straight line passing through (0, 0), such
 that for each point on the line the x-coordinate equals the y-
 coordinate, is**

  $y = x$

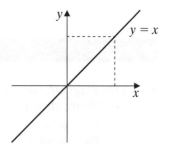

■ **The equation of the straight line passing through (0, 0), such
 that for each point on the line the x-coordinate equals the
 negative of the y-coordinate, is**

  $y = -x$

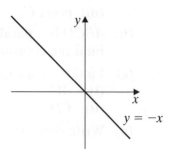

■ **The equation of any straight line passing through (0, 0) is always either**

$y =$ **a positive number times** x $(y = ax)$

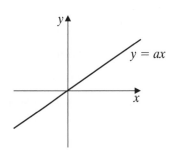

or

$y =$ **a negative number times** x $(y = -ax)$

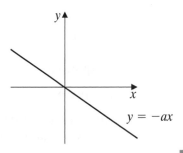

Exercise 7B

1 **(a)** Plot the points with coordinates
      $(0, 0)$ $(1, 1)$ $(2, 2)$ $(3, 3)$ $(-5, -5)$
   (b) Join these points with a straight line.
   (c) Write down the equation of the straight line.

2
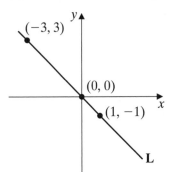

   Write down the equation of the line marked **L**.

3 **(a)** Plot the points with coordinates
      $(0, 0)$ $(3, 6)$ $(-2, -4)$
   (b) Join these points with a straight line.
   (c) Find the equation of this straight line.

4 **(a)** Plot the points with coordinates
      $(0, 0)$ $(1, -3)$ $(-2, 6)$
   (b) Join these points with a straight line.
   (c) Find the equation of this straight line.

5 Draw the line with equation

      $y = 5x$

7.3 General straight line graphs

Teaching reference:
pp 140–142, 150–155,
sections 9.2, 9.5

■ Every straight line graph will have an equation of the form

$$y = mx + c$$

where m and c are numbers.
For example, the following will give rise to straight line graphs:

$$y = 3x + 2$$
$$y = -2x + 7$$
$$y = \tfrac{1}{2}x - 1$$

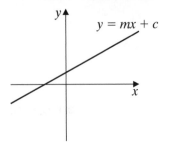

■ In the equation

$$y = mx + c$$

the value of c represents the height at which the straight line graph crosses the vertical (y) axis.

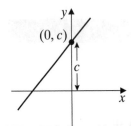

i.e. the graph crosses the y-axis at the point with coordinates $(0, c)$.

■ In the equation

$$y = mx + c$$

the value of m represents the increase in the y value caused by an increase of ONE in the x value.

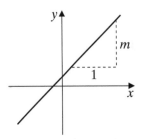

■ Straight line graphs can be used to solve equations such as $5x - 2 = 7$.

Example 2

The equation of a graph is

$$y = 3x - 1$$

(a) Copy and complete the table of values for $y = 3x - 1$:

x		-3	-2	-1	0	1	2	3
$y = 3x - 1$			-7			2		

(b) Draw the graph of $y = 3x - 1$ for values of x from -3 to 3.

(c) Use your graph to find the value of y when $x = 2.4$.

(d) Use your graph to solve the equation $3x - 1 = -3$.

(a) When $x = 3$, $y = 3x - 1 = 3 \times 3 - 1$ $= 9 - 1$ $= 8$

When $x = 2$, $y = 3x - 1 = 3 \times 2 - 1$ $= 6 - 1$ $= 5$

When $x = 0$, $y = 3x - 1 = 3 \times 0 - 1$ $= 0 - 1$ $= -1$

When $x = -1$, $y = 3x - 1 = 3 \times -1 - 1 = -3 - 1 = -4$

When $x = -3$, $y = 3x - 1 = 3 \times -3 - 1 = -9 - 1 = -10$

Note: as x increases by 1, y increases by 3.

$$y = 3x - 1$$

So the completed table of values is:

x	-3	-2	-1	0	1	2	3
y	-10	-7	-4	-1	2	5	8

(b)

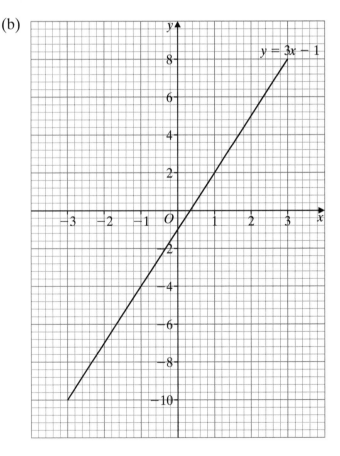

(c) From the graph: when $x = 2.4$, $y = 6.2$.

(d) To solve the equation $3x - 1 = -3$, we need to find out when the graph of $y = 3x - 1$ is equal to $y = -3$, i.e.:

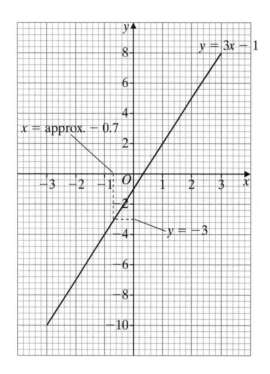

This gives an x value of $x = -0.7$ (to one decimal place).

Example 3

Draw the graph of $y = 2x + 3$.

When $x = 0$, $y = 2 \times x + 3 = 2 \times 0 + 3 = 0 + 3 = 3$.
So the graph passes through the point $(0, 3)$.

Increase x by 1, i.e. from 0 to 1.
When $x = 1$, $y = 2 \times x + 3 = 2 \times 1 + 3 = 2 + 3 = 5$.
So the graph passes through the point $(1, 5)$.

The graph of $y = 2x + 3$ is a straight line (of the type $y = mx + c$).

So the graph is:

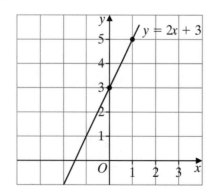

Exercise 7C

1 (a) Copy and complete the table for the equation $y = 2x + 3$:

x	-3	-2	-1	0	1	2	3
$y = 2x + 3$	-3				5		

(b) Draw the graph of $y = 2x + 3$ for values of x from -3 to 3.

2 (a) Copy and complete the table for the equation $y = \frac{1}{2}x + 5$:

x	-6	-4	-2	0	1	2	4	6
y	2			5			7	

(b) Draw the graph of $y = \frac{1}{2}x + 5$ for values of x from -6 to 6.
(c) Using your graph, or otherwise, find the value of:
   (i) y when $x = -1.6$ (ii) x when $y = 6.5$.

3 (a) Copy and complete the table of values for the equation $y = 12 - 5x$:

x	-2	-1	0	1	2	3
$y = 12 - 5x$		17			2	

(b) Draw the graph of $y = 12 - 5x$ for values of x from -2 to 3.
(c) Using your graph, or otherwise, work out the value of y when $x = 1.2$.
(d) Using your graph, or otherwise, solve these equations:
   (i) $12 - 5x = 0$ (ii) $12 - 5x = 10$.

4 Draw the graph of $y = 3x - 5$.

5 (a) Copy and complete the table of values for the equation $y = \frac{1}{2}x + 4$:

x	-2	-1	0	1	2
$y = \frac{1}{2}x + 4$		$3\frac{1}{2}$			

(b) Draw the graph of $y = \frac{1}{2}x + 4$.

6 Draw the graph of $y = 15 - 3x$.

7 Draw the graph of $y = \frac{1}{2}x - 5$.

8 Draw the graph of $y = 2 - \frac{1}{3}x$.

9 (a) Copy and complete the table of values for $y = 2x + 1$:

x	-4	-3	-2	-1	0	1	2	3
y								

(b) Draw the graph of $y = 2x + 1$.
(c) On the same axes, draw the graph of $y = x$.
(d) Write down the coordinates of the point where the two graphs meet.

7.4 Straight line graphs in real life

Teaching reference: pp 143–149, sections 9.3, 9.4

■ A function such as

$ax + b$ (where a and b are numbers)

gives rise to a straight line graph and is called a *linear function*.

■ Many linear functions and straight line graphs occur in real-life situations.

Example 4

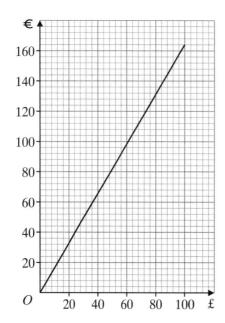

The graph above can be used for converting between pounds sterling (£) and Euros (€).

(a) Use the graph to convert £150 to Euros.

Alicia came back from holiday in Tenerife with €48.

(b) Using the conversion graph, or otherwise, convert €48 to pounds sterling.

Before the introduction of the Euro, the unit of currency on Tenerife was the peseta. £1 = 265 pesetas.

(c) Convert 15 000 pesetas to Euros.

(a) From the graph,

£100 = €164   £50 = €82

so

£150 = €164 + €82 = €246

(b) From the graph €48 = £29.5 (using the graph we can do no better than 1 d.p.)

so €48 = £29.50

(c) We divide pesetas by 265 to give pounds:

15 000 ÷ 265 = £57 (to nearest pound)

From the conversion graph, £57 = €93.

Example 5

The instructions for cooking a turkey are as follows:

Allow 45 minutes per kilogram, then add an extra 30 minutes.

(a) Work out the time, in minutes, to cook a turkey weighing 4 kg.
(b) Find a formula for the time t (minutes) to cook a turkey weighing x kilograms.
(c) Complete the table below for cooking times:

Weight (kg)	2	4	6	8	10	12
Time (min)						

(d) Draw the graph of cooking time against weight.
(e) Comment on the graph.

(a)   Time is $45 \times 4 + 30 = 180 + 30 = 210$ minutes

(b)   Time $= 45 \times$ weight $+ 30$, so
$$t = 45 \times x + 30 \qquad \text{or} \quad t = 45x + 30$$

(c) The times for the weights are

$45 \times 2 + 30 = 120$	$45 \times 4 + 30 = 210$	$45 \times 6 + 30 = 300$
$45 \times 8 + 30 = 390$	$45 \times 10 + 30 = 480$	$45 \times 12 + 30 = 570$

So the completed table is:

Weight (kg)	2	4	6	8	10	12
Time (min)	120	210	300	390	480	570

(d)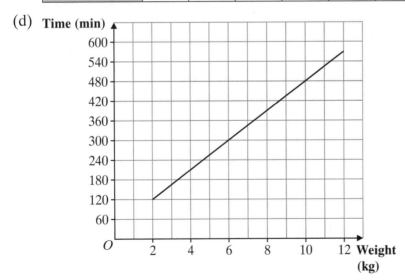

(e) The graph is of a linear function, so is a straight line graph.
The weight cannot be negative.
It would be pointless to extend the line back to where it crosses the vertical axis, because this would imply the existence a turkey of zero weight.

Exercise 7D

1

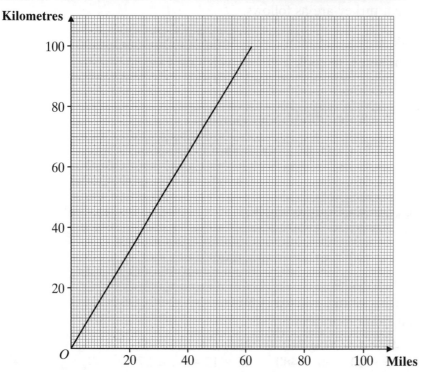

The graph above can be used for converting between kilometres and miles.

(a) Use the graph to convert 100 km to miles.

(b) Use the graph to convert 240 miles to km.

The maximum speed limit in the United Kingdom is 70 miles per hour.

The maximum speed limit in France is 120 kilometres per hour.

(c) Which of these two speed limits is the greater, and by how much?

2 The cost of hiring a car from Alpha Cars is
£15 per day plus 20 pence per mile.

(a) Work out the cost of hiring the car for a day and travelling 100 miles.

(b) Complete the table below for the total cost of hiring a car for a day and travelling different numbers of miles:

Miles	50	100	150	200	250	300
Total cost (£)						

(c) Draw the graph of the total cost against distance travelled.

Alan hired a car from Alpha Cars for a day. He travelled
x miles. The total cost to Alan is £y.

(d) Write down a formula connecting x and y.

The cost of hiring a car from Betta Cars for the day is fixed at
£40 per day, with no extra costs for the miles travelled.

(e) Using your graph, or otherwise, find the distance for
which the total cost with Alpha Cars is equal to the cost
with Betta Cars.

3

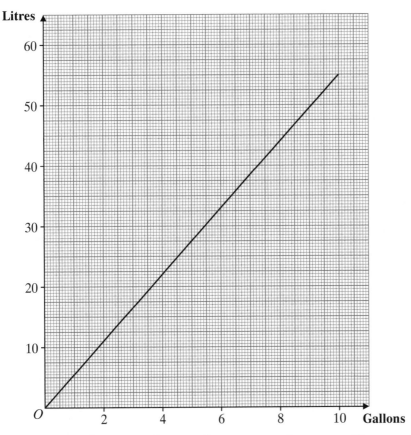

The graph above can be used to convert between litres and gallons.

(a) Convert 6 gallons to litres.

(b) Convert 50 litres to gallons.

Mrs Smith's oil tank holds 900 litres.

(c) Convert 900 litres to gallons.

4   James works as a plumber. He charges a fixed call-out fee of
£25 plus £12 for each hour he works.

(a) Copy and complete the table for the total charge:

Hours	1	2	3	4	5	6	7	8
Total charge (£)								

(b) Draw the graph of total charge against hours.

(c) Using the symbols

> y to represent total charge and
> x to represent the number of hours

find the equation of the graph.

James worked at Mrs Akram's house. The total charge to Mrs
Akram was £79.

(d) Using your graph, or otherwise, find the number of hours
James worked at Mrs Akram's house.

7.5 Interpreting other graphs

■ **Interpretations can be made from many types of graph arising from real-life situations.**

Teaching reference:
pp 143–149, sections 9.3, 9.4

Example 6

The diagram represents a bottle.

Water is poured into the bottle at a steady rate.

Sketch a graph of the height of the water in the bottle against time.

Because the bottle is wide at the bottom the height of the water will rise slowly to start with. But the height will increase more rapidly as the bottle gets fuller.

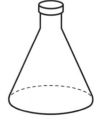

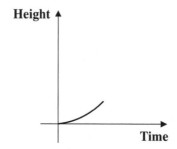

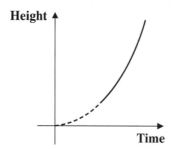

So the overall sketch graph will be:

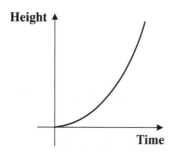

Worked examination question (modified)

Barry's pulse rate is taken every six hours over 3 days:

(a) Write down the first pulse rate shown on the graph.
(b) Write down Barry's highest pulse rate during the three days.
(c) Work out the difference between the highest and lowest pulse rates shown on 3rd May.
(d) Comment on the overall trend for these pulse rates.

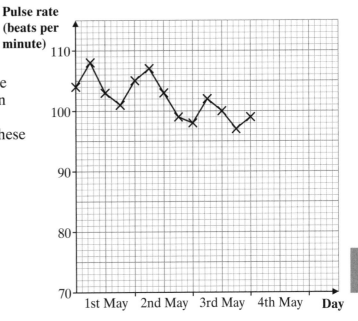

(a) The first pulse rate shown is 104 beats per minute.
(b) The highest pulse rate shown is 108 beats per minute.
(c) The difference between highest and lowest on 3rd May is $102 - 97 = 5$ beats per minute.
(d) Whilst there are daily variations between highest and lowest, the overall trend is downwards, as indicated by the sketch of the trend line.

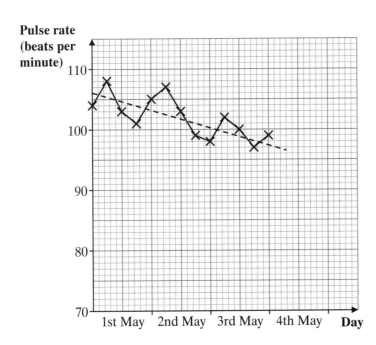

Exercise 7E

1   Lester ran a 100 metres sprint in 10 seconds.
    The graph of his speed against time is shown below.

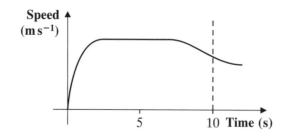

Comment as fully as possible on his speed during the sprint.

2   The diagram represents a goldfish bowl.

Water is poured into the bowl at a steady rate.
Draw a sketch of the height of the water against time.

3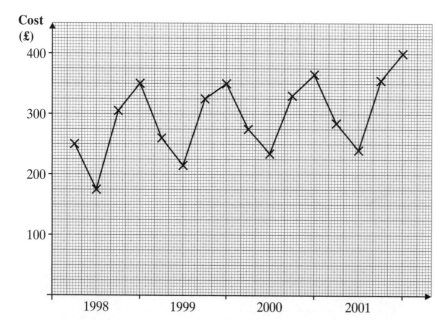

The diagram represents Gemma's quarterly gas bill over the
four year period from 1998 to 2001.
(a) Write down her highest gas bill during this period.
(b) Comment on the overall trend in these gas bills.

4 Helen threw a rounders ball.

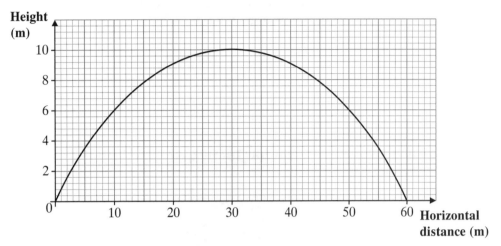

The graph above shows the height of the ball above the ground against the horizontal distance travelled by the ball.
(a) How far did the ball travel horizontally?
(b) Find the maximum height of the ball above the ground.
(c) Find the height of the ball above the ground when it has travelled 12 metres.

Summary of key points

- You can describe positions on a grid using coordinates.

- Lines parallel to the x-axis have equations y = a constant.

- Lines parallel to the y-axis have equations x = a constant.

- The mid-point of the line segment joining (a, b) and (c, d) is $\left(\dfrac{a + c}{2}, \dfrac{b + d}{2}\right)$

- The equation of the straight line passing through $(0, 0)$, such that for each point on the line the x-coordinate equals the y-coordinate, is

    $y = x$

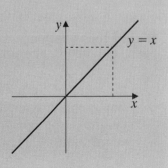

■ **The equation of the straight line passing through (0, 0), such that for each point on the line the *x*-coordinate equals the negative of the *y*-coordinate, is**

$$y = -x$$

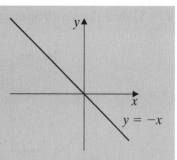

■ **The equation of any straight line passing through (0, 0) is always either**

$y = $ **a positive number times** x $(y = ax)$

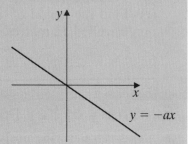

or

$y = $ **a negative number times** x $(y = -ax)$

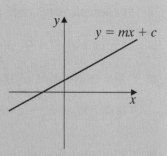

■ **Every straight line graph will have an equation of the form**

$$y = mx + c$$

where *m* and *c* are numbers.
For example, the following will give rise to straight line graphs:

$$y = 3x + 2$$
$$y = -2x + 7$$
$$y = \tfrac{1}{2}x - 1$$

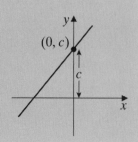

■ **In the equation**

$$y = mx + c$$

the value of *c* represents the height at which the straight line graph crosses the vertical (*y*) axis.
i.e. the graph crosses the *y*-axis at the point with coordinates (0, *c*).

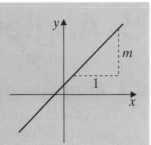

- In the equation

  $$y = mx + c$$

  the value of m represents the increase in the y value caused by an increase of ONE in the x value.

  Straight line graphs can be used to solve equations such as $5x - 2 = 7$.

- A function such as

  $$ax + b \text{ (where } a \text{ and } b \text{ are numbers)}$$

  gives rise to a straight line graph and is called a *linear function*.

- Many linear functions and straight line graphs occur in real-life situations.

- Interpretations can be made from many types of graph arising from real-life situations.

8 Angles, geometry and proof

8.1 Alternate and corresponding angles

Teaching reference:
pp 59–61, section 3.9

- The shaded angles are equal.
  They are called *alternate angles*.

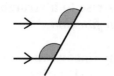 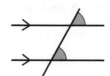

- The shaded angles are equal.
  They are called *corresponding angles*.

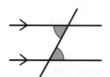

Example 1

Work out the marked angles in the diagram.
Give reasons for your answers.

$a = 73°$ (corresponding angles)

$b = a = 73°$ (alternate angles)

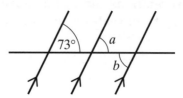

Exercise 8A   **Links 3I**

In questions **1–8** work out the size of the marked angles.
Give reasons for your answers.

1

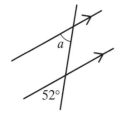

2

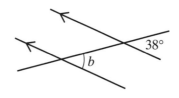

3

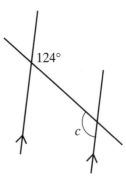

4

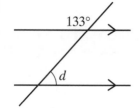

5

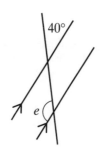

6

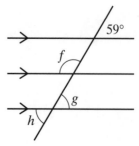

7

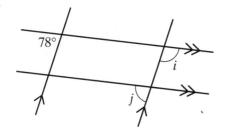

8

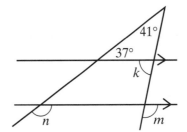

9

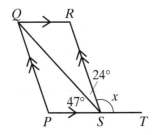

PQRS is a parallelogram.
Angle *QSP* = 47°.
Angle *QSR* = 24°.
PST is a straight line.
(a) Find the size of the angle marked *x*.
Give a reason for your answer.
(b) Work out the size of angle *PQS*.
Give a reason for your answer.

(E)

10

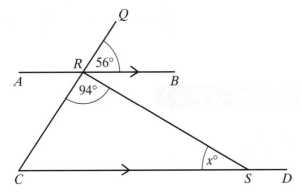

In the diagram the lines *AB* and *CD* are parallel.
CRQ is a straight line.
Angle *CRS* = 94°.
Angle *QRB* = 56°.
Angle *RSC* = *x*°.
Find the value of *x*.

(E)

8.2 Parallelograms and proof

Teaching reference:
p 62, section 3.10

Proof 1   Opposite angles in a parallelogram are equal

x = angle *BAC* = angle *ACD*   (alternate angles)
y = angle *CAD* = angle *BCA*   (alternate angles)
$x + y$ = angle *A* = angle *C*

Opposite angles of a parallelogram are equal.

Proof 2 Angles in a triangle add up to 180°

Draw a line XAY parallel to the base BC. Then

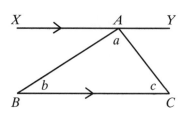

    angle XAB = angle $ABC = b$ (alternate angles)

    angle YAC = angle $ACB = c$ (alternate angles)

    and angle $BAC = a$

The angles in the triangle are a, b and c.
The angles which make straight line XAY are a, b and c.

Therefore the angles in a triangle add up to 180°.

Proof 3 The exterior angle of a triangle is equal to the sum of the interior and opposite angles

$$c = a + b$$

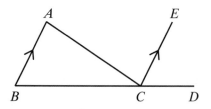

   Draw CE parallel to AB:

angle BAC = angle ACE (alternate angles)

angle ABC = angle ECD (corresponding angles)

Adding these together:
angle BAC + angle ABC = angle ACD

Exercise 8B

1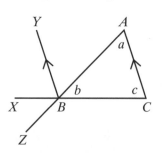

ABC is a straight line.
Show that angle $ABD = a + b$.
Give reasons.

2

XBC and ZBA are straight lines.
Show that angle $YBZ = b + c$.
Give reasons.

3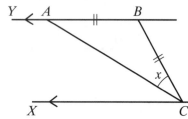

$AB = BC$.
Angle $BCA = x$.
(a) Write down angle BAC in terms of x.
(b) Show that AC bisects angle BCX.
Give reasons.

4 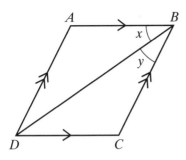 *ABCD* is a parallelogram.
Show that angle *A* = angle *C*.

5 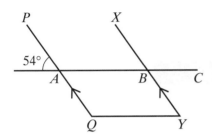 *ABC* is a straight line.
Explain why angle *CBY* = 54°.
(Hint: there are two steps.)

6 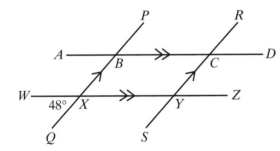 *PQ* is parallel to *RS*.
AD is parallel to *WZ*.
Explain why angle *RCD* = 48°.

7 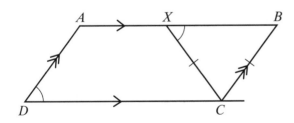 *ABCD* is a parallelogram.
XC = *BC*.
Explain why angle *BXC* = angle *D*.

8 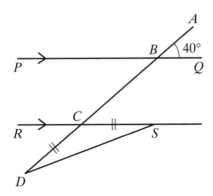 *ABCD* is a straight line.
PQ is parallel to *RS*.
CD = *CS*.
Show, with reasons, that
angle *CSD* = 20°.

8.3 Chord, tangent and arc

■ A straight line crossing a circle is called a *chord*.

■ A section of the circumference is called an *arc*.

■ A straight line that touches a circle is called a *tangent*.

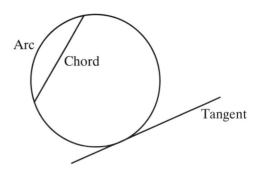

Exercise 8C

1 Use a pair of compasses to draw a circle.
Mark an arc on the circumference.
At each end of the arc, *P* and *Q*, draw a tangent to the circle.
T is the point where the tangents meet.

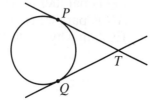

Join *PQ*, *PT* and *QT*.
What is the mathematical name for *PQ*?
What can you say about triangle *PQT*?

2 Draw two circles of different size as shown in the diagram.
Draw the common tangents to meet at *O*.
What can you say about *AX* and *BY*?

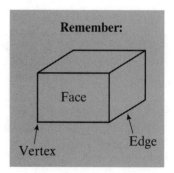

3 Repeat question **2** with non-intersecting circles.

8.4 Explore the geometry of cubes and cuboids

Example 2

How many planes of symmetry does this shape have?

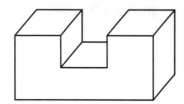

Remember:

Face

Edge

Vertex

It has two planes of symmetry:

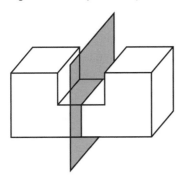 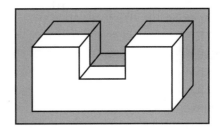

Exercise 8D   Links 18E

1 Show all of the planes of symmetry on a copy of this cuboid.

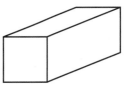

2 How many planes of symmetry does a cube have?

3 Say how many planes of symmetry each of these shapes has.
The shapes are made from cubes.

(a) 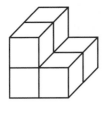 **(b)** 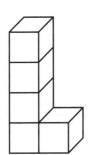 **(c)**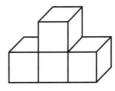

(d) 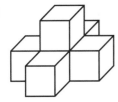 **(e)**

4 The diagram shows a prism.
Copy the diagram and draw one plane of symmetry.

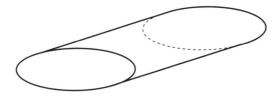

(E)

5   Copy and draw in one plane of symmetry for each of these shapes.

(i)

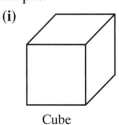

Cube

(ii)

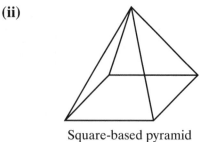

Square-based pyramid

(E)

8.5 Drawing on isometric grids

Example 3

Sketch a 1 cm cube on an isometric grid.

Draw one face, (in this case, the top).

Complete the drawing.

It can also be drawn this way round.

Exercise 8E

1   The diagram shows 3 possible ways of drawing the letter L on an isometric grid:

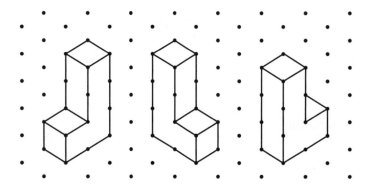

On isometric paper, draw I, T, F, E and H made from centimetre cubes.

2 The measurements of the cuboid on Grid A are 3 cm by 2 cm by 1 cm. Draw a cuboid with measurements that are double the measurements of the cuboid on Grid A. [E]

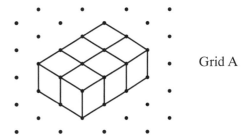

Grid A

3

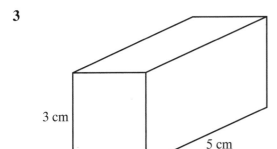

3 cm

5 cm

2 cm

On an isometric grid, make an accurate full-size drawing of the cuboid in the diagram. (E)

8.6 Cross-sections, plan and elevation

Teaching reference:
pp 182–183, 188–190,
sections 11.4, 11.6

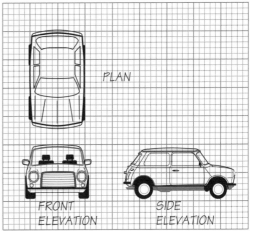

- ■ The plan of a solid is the view when seen from above.

- ■ The front elevation is the view when seen from the front.

- ■ The side elevation is the view when seen from the side.

- ■ A cross-section is the surface you get when you make a cut through a solid shape.

Example 4

Draw the plan and elevations of this shape:

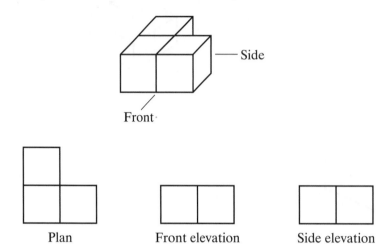

Side

Front

Plan
(seen from above)

Front elevation

Side elevation

Exercise 8F   **Links 11H**

1 Draw the plans and elevations of these shapes:

(a) **(b)**

(c) **(d)**

(e) **(f)**

(g) **(h)**

2   For each plan and elevation shown:

  (i) make the shape from multicubes,

 (ii) draw the solid on an isometric grid.

Plan	Front elevation	Right side elevation

(a)

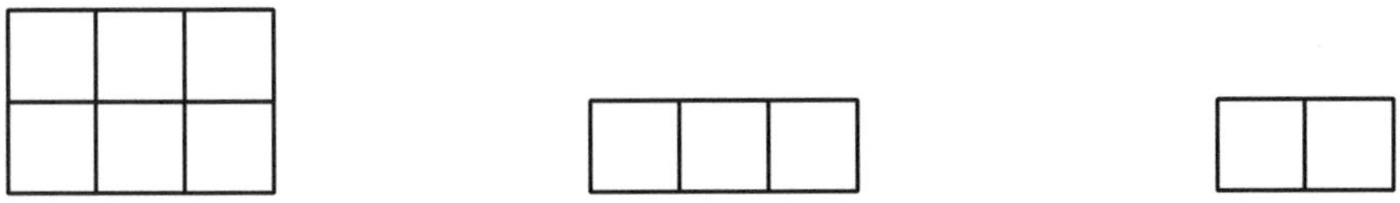

(b)

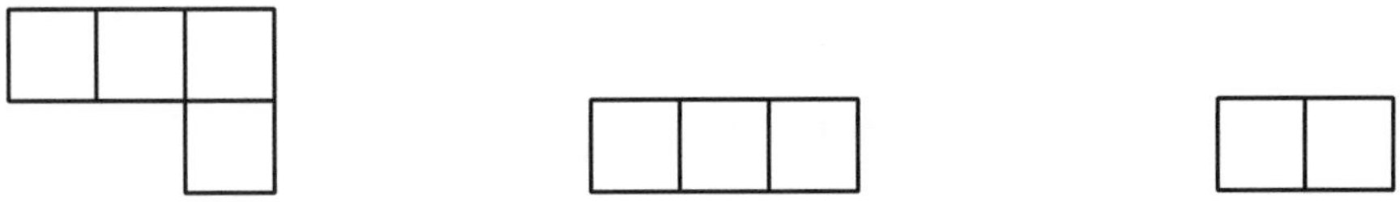

(c)

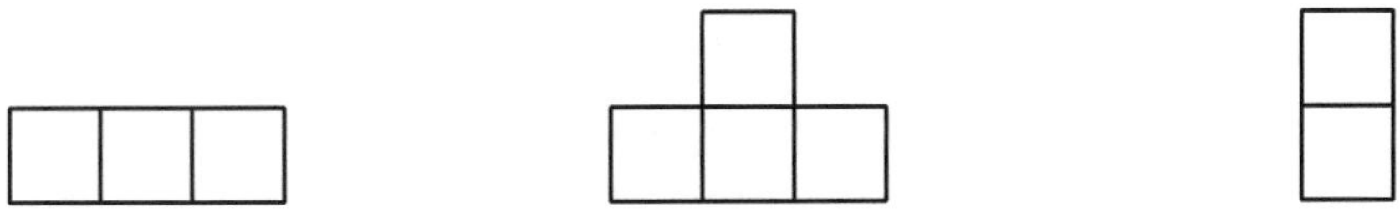

(d)

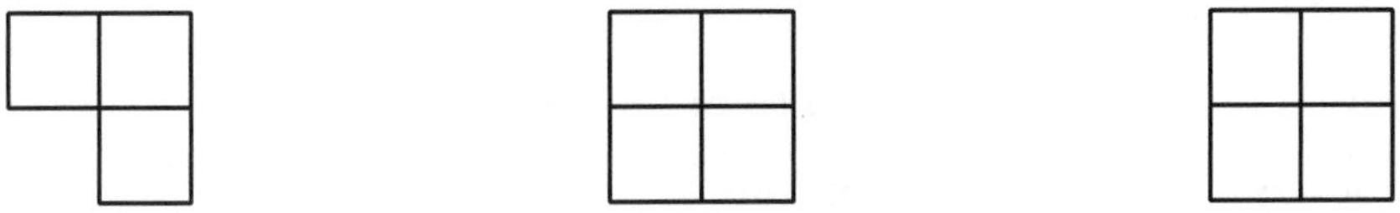

(e)

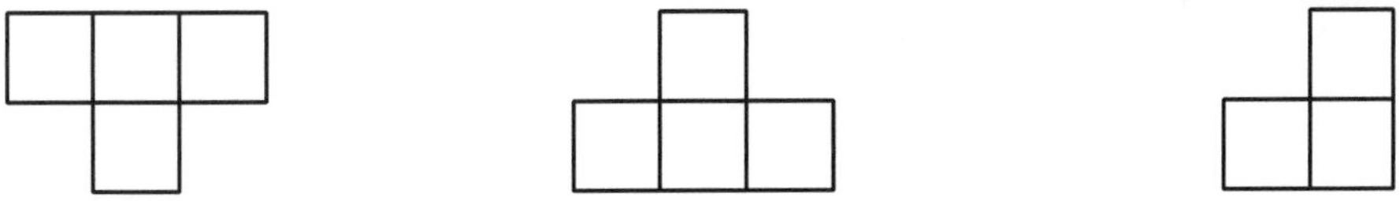

(f)

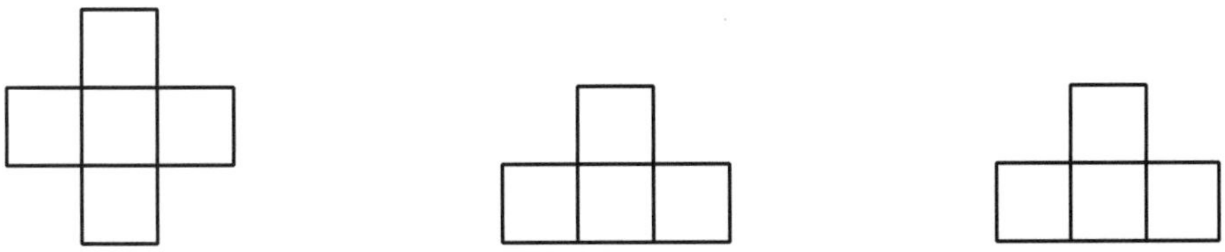

(g)

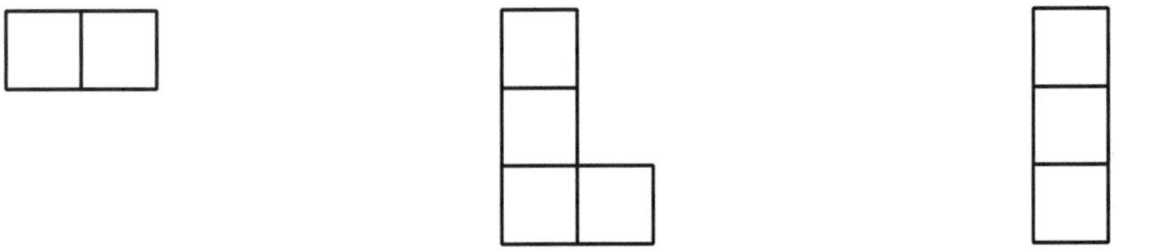

Summary of key points

- The shaded angles are equal.
  They are called *alternate angles*.

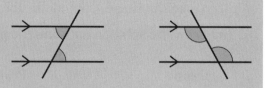

- The shaded angles are equal.
  They are called *corresponding angles*.

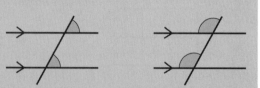

- A straight line crossing a circle is called a *chord*.

- A section of the circumference is called an *arc*.

- A straight line that touches a circle is called
  a *tangent*.

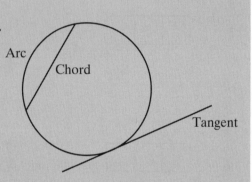

- The plan of a solid is the view when seen from above.

- The front elevation is the view when seen from the front.

- The side elevation is the view when seen from the side.

- A cross-section is the surface you get when you make a cut
  through a solid shape.

9 Transformations, and using scales in accurate maps and drawings

9.1 Symmetry in 3-D shapes

■ A plane of symmetry separates a 3-D shape into two equal halves which are mirror images of each other.

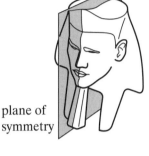

plane of symmetry

Example 1

Copy this cuboid and draw all its planes of symmetry:

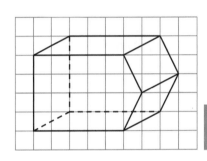

Here are the planes of symmetry:

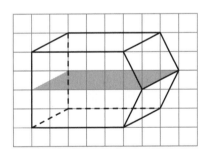

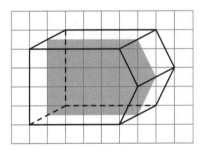

Exercise 9A   Links (*18E*) 18E

You may use squared paper and tracing paper in this exercise.

1   Copy or trace the following shapes and clearly mark any planes of symmetry on your drawings:

(a)   (b)   (c)   (d)

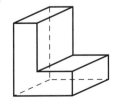

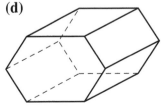

2 The drawings on the right show half a 3-D solid.
Copy and complete each solid so that the shaded face forms a plane of symmetry.

(a)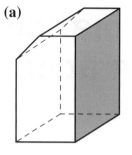

(b)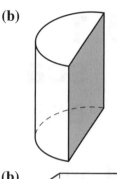

3 Copy or trace each shape.
Draw in the number of planes of symmetry indicated for each shape.

(a)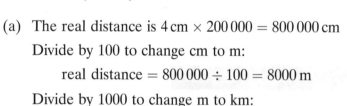

(b)

1 plane   3 planes

9.2 Using scales in accurate maps and drawings

■ **A scale is a ratio which shows the relationship between a length on a drawing and the actual length in real life.**

> There is more about ratio in unit 3.

Example 2

The scale on this road map is 1 : 200 000.

Sheffield and Chesterfield are 4 cm apart on the map.

(a) Work out the real distance, in km, between Sheffield and Chesterfield.

(b) Measure the distance between Sheffield and Rotherham on the map, and work out the real distance, in km, between them.

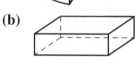

(a) The real distance is 4 cm × 200 000 = 800 000 cm

Divide by 100 to change cm to m:

real distance = 800 000 ÷ 100 = 8000 m

Divide by 1000 to change m to km:

real distance = 8000 ÷ 1000

So real distance between Sheffield and Chesterfield = 8 km.

(b) The measured distance between Sheffield and Rotherham = 3.5 cm.

So real distance = 3.5 cm × 200 000 = 700 000 cm

Divide by 100 to change cm to m: = 7000 m

Divide by 1000 to change m to km: = 7 km

So real distance between Sheffield and Rotherham = 7 km.

Example 3

St Albans is 5 km due west of Hatfield. Welwyn is 6 km due north of Hatfield.

> You will need a ruler and protractor.

(a) Make a scale drawing to show the three towns. Use a scale of 1 : 100 000.

(b) Use your drawing to find the real distance from Welwyn to St Albans.

(a) 1 : 100 000 means 1 cm on the map represents 100 000 cm in real life.

$$100\,000\,\text{cm} = 1000\,\text{m} = 1\,\text{km}$$

Therefore 1 cm on the map represents 1 km.

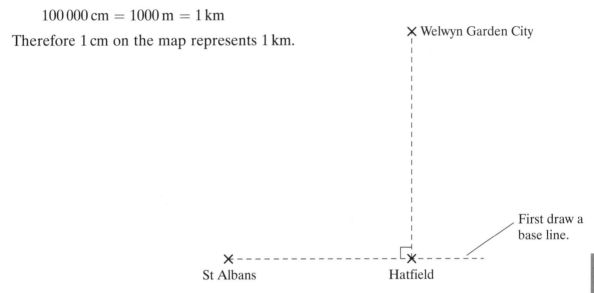

(b) Welwyn to St Albans = 8 cm on the map.

$$\text{Real distance} = 8 \times 100\,000\,\text{cm} \qquad = 800\,000\,\text{cm}$$

divide by 100 000 to change cm to km: $= 8\,\text{km}$

Exercise 9B   Links (*17E*) 17E

1   A map has a scale of 1 : 50 000.
    What is the real distance when the distance on the map is:
    (a) 6 cm   (b) 3 cm   (c) 4.5 cm
    (d) 7.5 cm   (e) 8.6 cm   (f) 12.1 cm?

2   A builder draws the plan of a house using a scale of 1 : 125.
    (a) Measure the sides.
    (b) Copy and put the real measurements on the diagram.

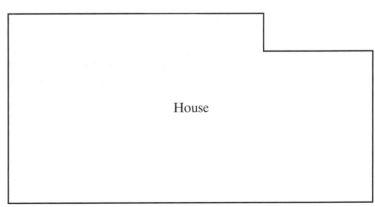

3 A map is drawn to a scale of 1 : 200 000. Work out the real length of a reservoir which is 3.5 cm long on the map.

4

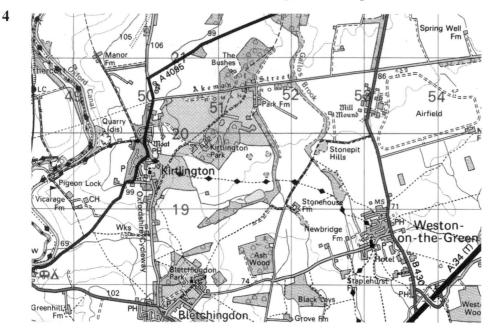

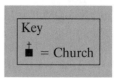

© Crown copyright, Licence no. 100000230

On the map the scale is 1 : 50 000.

(a) Use the map to work out the distance between Weston-on-the-Green church and Bletchingdon church.

(b) Draw a scale diagram to show the villages of Bletchingdon, Weston-on-the-Green and Kirtlington. Use a scale of 1 : 25 000.

5 Clifton is 8 km due south of Sandy.
Sandy is 10 km due east of Bedford.

(a) Make a scale drawing to show the three towns. Use a scale of 1 : 100 000.

(b) Use your drawing to find the real distance from Bedford to Clifton.

Summary of key points

■ A plane of symmetry separates a 3-D shape into two equal halves which are mirror images of each other.

■ A scale is a ratio which shows the relationship between a length on a drawing and the actual length in real life.

10 Similarity, congruence and nets

10.1 Enlargement and similarity

Teaching reference:
pp 348–353, section 22.4

Activity

Look at the shapes below.
(a) (i) Put them into sets of circles, squares and rectangles.
   (ii) Describe the transformation between each shape in each set (if one can be found).

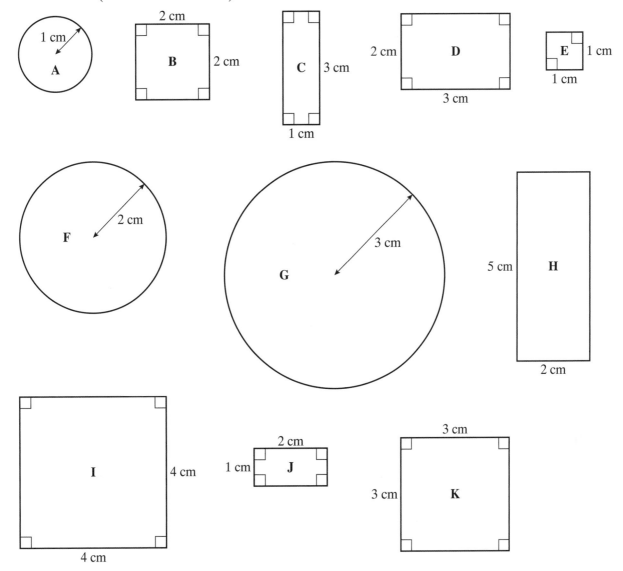

(b) Which shapes are similar and which are not?

10.2 Congruent triangles

■ **For triangles to be congruent they must demonstrate:**

SAS (side, angle, side)

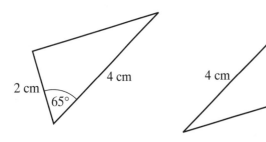

> Note: 'congruent' means the same shape and also the same size.

> Two sides and the enclosed angle the same.

ASA (angle, side, angle)

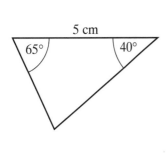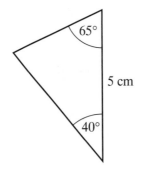

SSS (side, side, side)

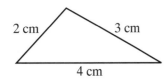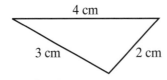

RHS (right angle, hypotenuse, side)

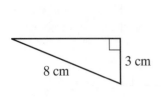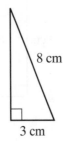

Example 1

(a) Write down the letters of the congruent triangles.
(b) Give a reason for your answer.

A
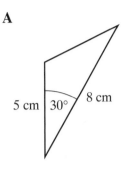

B
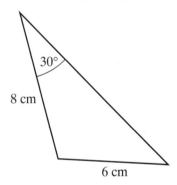

C
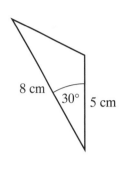

(a) **A** and **C** are congruent.
(b) Side, angle, side (SAS).

Example 2

Draw diagrams to show why two triangles, both with the following
measurements, are not necessarily congruent:

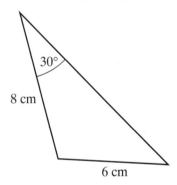

Because the angle given is not in between the two sides, two
different triangles may share these measurements:

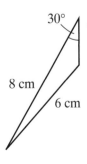

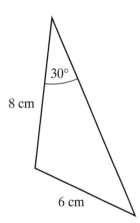

Exercise 10A   Links 5E

1   For each group of triangles write down the letters of the
    congruent triangles. Give a reason for your answer.
    (a)

A
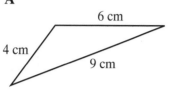
6 cm
4 cm
9 cm

B
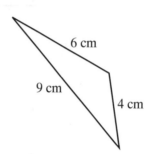
6 cm
9 cm
4 cm

C
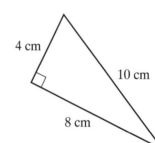
4 cm
10 cm
8 cm

(b)

A
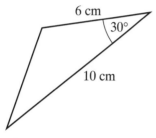
6 cm
30°
10 cm

B
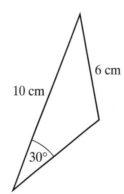
6 cm
10 cm
30°

C
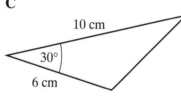
10 cm
30°
6 cm

(c)

A
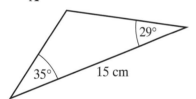
29°
35°
15 cm

B
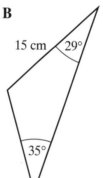
15 cm
29°
35°

C
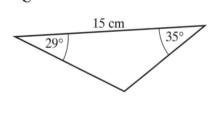
15 cm
29°
35°

(d) **A**
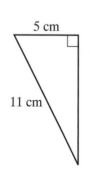
5 cm
11 cm

B
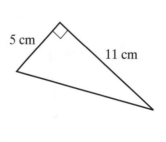
5 cm
11 cm

C
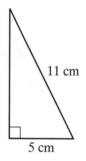
11 cm
5 cm

2   For each pair of triangles state whether they are congruent,
and give a reason if they are.

(a)

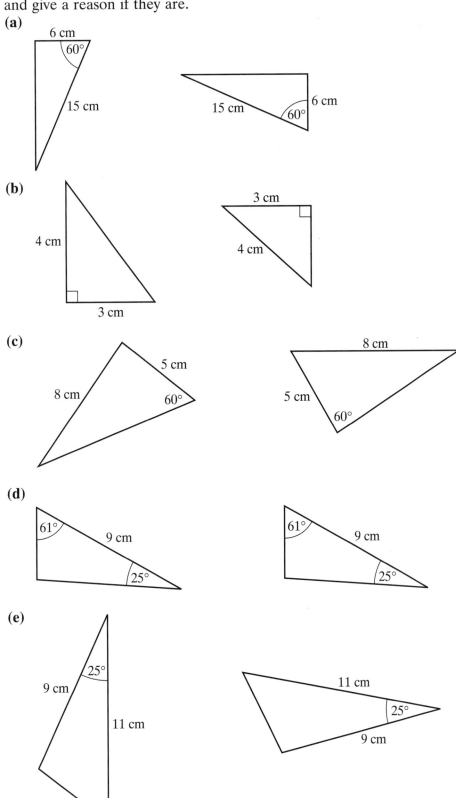

3 In **(a)** and **(b)**, draw diagrams to show why two triangles, both having the same measurements shown, are not necessarily congruent:

(a)

(b)

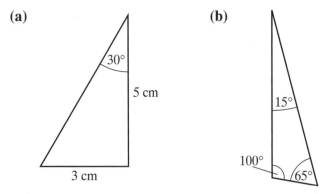

10.3 Nets

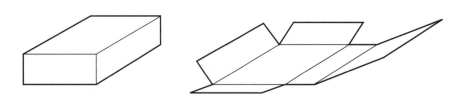

The box (cuboid) in the pictures has been opened out to make a 2-D shape. This 2-D shape is called the *net* of the box.

■ **A net is a 2-D shape that can be made into a 3-D shape.**

Example 3
Draw the accurate net of this square-based pyramid:

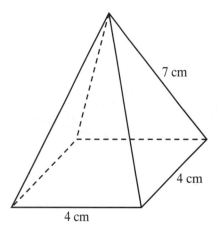

Use a pair of compasses and a ruler to construct this net.

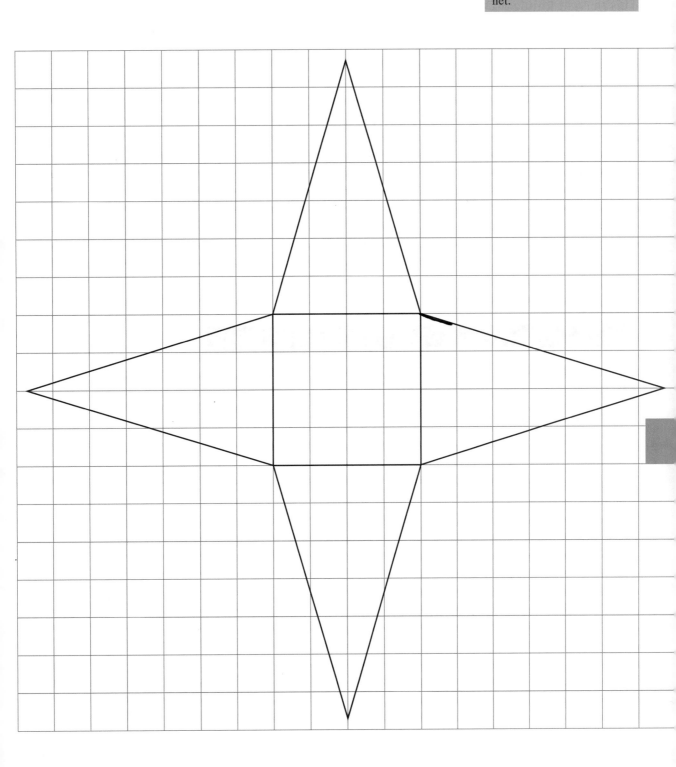

Example 4

This net will form a 3-D solid.   Draw a sketch of the solid.

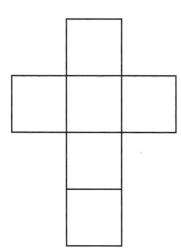

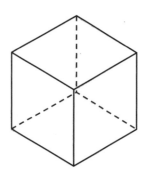

> This solid is called a cube.

You will need a ruler and a pair of compasses for some of the questions in this exercise.

1 Draw accurate nets of these shapes:

(a)

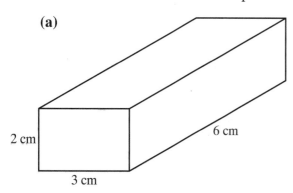

2 cm

6 cm

3 cm

(b)

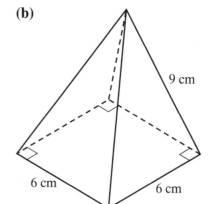

9 cm

6 cm   6 cm

(c)

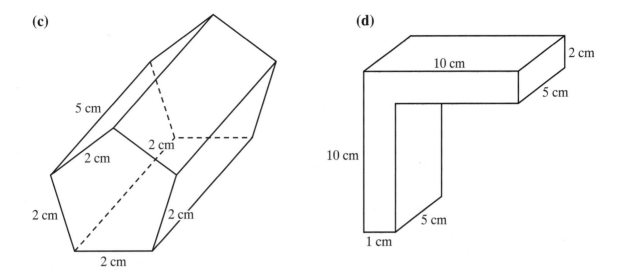

(d)

2   These nets will each form a 3-D solid.
     Draw a sketch of each solid.

(a)

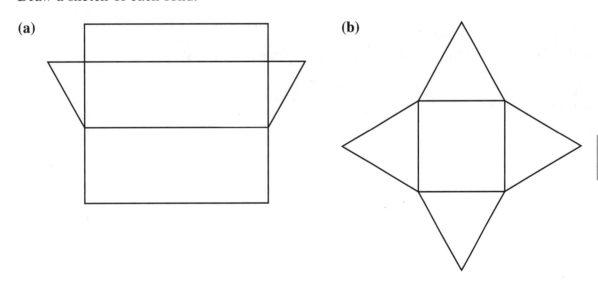

(b)

3   Find as many nets as possible which form the same cube.

4 Draw accurate nets for the following 3-D shapes:

    (a) a square-based pyramid, slant height 5 cm and base side 3 cm

    (b) a cube of side 4 cm

    (c) a prism of height 6 cm with the cross-section of an equilateral triangle of side 4 cm.

5 Copy and complete this net so that it will form a cuboid:

Summary of key points

■ For triangles to be congruent they must demonstrate **SAS, SSS, RHS** or **ASA**.

■ A net is a 2-D shape that can be made into a 3-D shape.

11 Mensuration

11.1 Metric equivalents

Metric	Imperial
8 km	5 miles
1 kg	2.2 pounds (lb)
25 g	1 ounce (oz)
1 litre (*l*)	1.75 pints
4.5 *l*	1 gallon
1 m	39 inches
30 cm	1 foot
2.5 cm	1 inch

Example 1

1 yard = 36 inches.
How many centimetres are there in a yard?

1 inch = 2.5 cm
1 yard = 36 inches = 36 × 2.5 cm = 90 cm

Exercise 11A   **Links 13E, 13F**

1 Change these weights into pounds (lb):
  (a) 7 kg   (b) 22 kg   (c) 39.2 kg
  (d) 4.07 kg   (e) 600 g

2 Change these weights into kilograms:
  (a) 3 lbs   (b) 150 lbs   (c) 96.5 lbs
  (d) 24.2 lbs   (e) 1 lb

3 There are 14 lbs in a stone.
  Bill weighs 12 stone 10 lbs.
  What is his weight in kilograms?

4 The distance from Doncaster to Edinburgh is 237 miles.
  How far is this in kilometres?

5 The horizon is approximately 42 kilometres away.
  How far is this in miles?

6 Mary measures out 15 litres of water using a 1 pint milk bottle.
  How many full bottles would she need?

7 Petrol costs 78.6p per litre.
  How much is this per gallon?

8 There are 16 ounces (oz) in a pound (lb).
A chicken weighs 3 lbs 5 oz.
How much does this chicken weigh in grams?

9 A plank of wood is 1.8 metres long.
What is its length in feet?

10 There are 12 inches in a foot.
Ajay is 5 feet 7 inches tall.
How tall is he in centimetres?

11.2 Converting units of area and volume

You are expected to know how to convert units of area and
volume, but if you are working out an area or volume it is best to
change to the units you want before doing the calculation.

Area

- $1 \text{ m}^2 = 100 \times 100 \text{ cm}^2 = 10\,000 \text{ cm}^2$

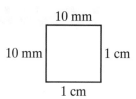

- $1 \text{ cm}^2 = 10 \times 10 \text{ mm}^2 = 100 \text{ mm}^2$

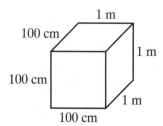

Volume

- $1 \text{ m}^3 = 100 \times 100 \times 100 \text{ cm}^3 = 1\,000\,000 \text{ cm}^3$

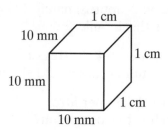

- $1 \text{ cm}^3 = 10 \times 10 \times 10 \text{ mm}^3 = 1000 \text{ mm}^3$

Example 2

The area of a stamp is $12\,\text{cm}^2$.
Write down its area in mm^2.

$$1\,\text{cm}^2 = 100\,\text{mm}^2$$

So $12\,\text{cm}^2 = 12 \times 100\,\text{mm}^2 = 1200\,\text{mm}^2$

Example 3

The volume of a small bottle is $35\,400\,\text{mm}^3$.
Write down its volume in cm^3.

$$1\,\text{cm}^3 = 1000\,\text{mm}^3$$

So $35\,400\,\text{mm}^3 = 35\,400 \div 1000\,\text{cm}^3 = 35.4\,\text{cm}^3$

Exercise 11B	**Links 19R**

1 Work out the number of:
   (a) cm^2 in $5\,\text{m}^2$ (b) cm^2 in $28\,\text{m}^2$
   (c) cm^2 in $1.2\,\text{m}^2$ (d) cm^2 in $105\,\text{m}^2$
   (e) m^2 in $26\,000\,\text{cm}^2$ (f) m^2 in $3400\,\text{cm}^2$
   (g) mm^2 in $8\,\text{cm}^2$ (h) mm^2 in $22\,\text{cm}^2$
   (i) cm^2 in $2400\,\text{mm}^2$ (j) cm^2 in $36\,200\,\text{mm}^2$.

2 Work out the number of:
   (a) cm^3 in $2.3\,\text{m}^3$ (b) cm^3 in $0.04\,\text{m}^3$
   (c) cm^3 in $0.304\,\text{m}^3$ (d) m^3 in $7\,000\,000\,\text{cm}^3$
   (e) m^3 in $530\,000\,\text{cm}^3$ (f) m^3 in $26\,500\,\text{cm}^3$
   (g) mm^3 in $4\,\text{cm}^3$ (h) mm^3 in $13.05\,\text{cm}^3$
   (i) cm^3 in $8400\,\text{mm}^3$ (j) cm^3 in $430\,\text{mm}^3$.

3 (a) Work out the surface area of each face in:
        (i) m^2 (ii) cm^2.
   (b) Work out the volume of the cuboid in:
        (i) m^3 (ii) cm^3.

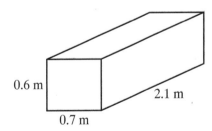

0.6 m   2.1 m

0.7 m

11.3 Area and circumference of circles

There are simple formulae for finding the area and circumference
of a circle.

- **Area** $= \pi r^2 = \pi \times r \times r$

- **Circumference** $= 2\pi r = 2 \times \pi \times r$ or $\pi \times d$

r is the radius and d is the
diameter.

Example 4

Find (a) the circumference and (b) the area of a circle with diameter 17 cm.

(a) Circumference $= \pi d = \pi \times 17 = 53.4$ cm (to 1 d.p.)

(b) Area $= \pi r^2$

Find the radius:

radius $=$ diameter $\div 2 = 17 \div 2 = 8.5$ cm

area $= \pi \times (8.5)^2 = 227$ cm^2 (to 3 s.f.)

Example 5

The area of a circular table top is 1.2 m^2.
Work out the circumference.

To do this you need to know the radius.

Area $= 1.2$ m$^2 = \pi r^2$

So $r^2 = \dfrac{1.2}{\pi}$ and $r = 0.618$ metres (61.8 cm) (3 s.f.)

Circumference $= 2\pi r = 2\pi \times 61.8$ cm $= 388$ cm (3 s.f.)

Exercise 11C   **Links 19D–G, M–O**

1   Work out the circumference and area of these circles:
     (a) radius 6 cm   (b) radius 14 cm
     (c) radius 8.3 cm   (d) radius 0.74 m
     (e) diameter 11.3 cm   (f) diameter 13.9 mm
     (g) diameter 1.6 m

2   The cross-section of a cable is a circle with diameter 2.5 cm.
     Work out the cross-sectional area.

3   The circumference of a circular pond is 25 metres.
     Work out its diameter and area.

4   A circle has a radius of 32 cm.
     Work out the circumference of the circle to the nearest cm.   (E)

11.4 Speed

■   Speed $= \dfrac{\text{distance}}{\text{time}}$

■   Averge speed $= \dfrac{\text{total distance}}{\text{total time}}$

    The formula is $v = \dfrac{s}{t}$ **where** $v =$ **speed**
                                        $s =$ **distance**
                                        $t =$ **time**

Common units for speed are m/s (metres per second)
km/h (kilometres per hour)
mph (miles per hour).

Example 6

The average speed for a journey of 273 km was 57.2 km/h.
How long did the journey take?

Rearranging the formula, $\text{time} = \dfrac{\text{distance}}{\text{speed}}$

$$\text{time} = \frac{273}{57.2} = 4.772\,727\,3 \text{ hours}$$

Notice that the answer is in hours because of the units being used.

Each hour is 60 minutes.
To change hours into minutes multiply by 60:

$0.772\,727\,3 \text{ hours} = 0.772\,727\,3 \times 60 = 46.4 \text{ minutes (1 d.p.)}$

So the journey took 4 hours 46.4 minutes.

Example 7

Ben travels 7.3 km in 8.5 minutes.
What is his average speed? As kilometres per minute is not a usual
combination of units, give your answer in (a) metres per second
and (b) kilometres per hour.

(a) $v = \dfrac{s}{t}$

So $\text{speed} = 7.3 \text{ km} \div 8.5 \text{ minutes}$

For an answer in metres per second change the units:

$7.3 \text{ km} = 7300 \text{ m and } 8.5 \text{ minutes} = 510 \text{ seconds}$

$$\text{speed} = 7300 \text{ m} \div 510 \text{ seconds}$$
$$= 14.3 \text{ m/s (1 d.p.)}$$

(b) $7.3 \text{ km} \div 8.5 \text{ minutes} = 0.859 \text{ km/min}$
$$= 0.859 \times 60 \text{ km/h}$$
$$= 51.5 \text{ km/h (1 d.p.)}$$

Exercise 11D

1 Copy and complete the table:

	Distance	Time	Average speed
(a)	128 km	2 h	
(b)	58 miles		8 mph
(c)		20 s	30 m/s
(d)	2.3 km	50 s	
(e)		$3\frac{1}{2}$ h	50 mph
(f)	165 km	$2\frac{1}{2}$ h	
(g)	750 m		25 m/s
(h)		$2\frac{1}{2}$ min	40 m/s
(i)	100 km	50 min	
(j)	254 miles	1 h 15 min	
(k)	76 km		15 km/h
(l)	27.15 km	16 min 10 s	
(m)	127 miles		55 mph
(n)		3 h 18 min	30 mph
(o)	2350 km	$1\frac{1}{2}$ days	

2 A car travels for 3 hours at an average speed of 43 mph. How far does it travel?

3 According to the railway timetable the distance between Edinburgh and Glasgow is 57 miles and the journey takes 1 hour 7 minutes.
What is the average speed for this journey?

4 The winner of a 100 m race took 9.3 seconds. What was his average speed?

5 How long does it take to do a journey of 190 kilometres at 55 km/h?

6 A skier averages 20 m/s for 6 minutes. How far does he travel?

7 How far would you travel in 13 minutes if your average speed was 28 km/h?

8 How long does it take to travel 185 km at 40 km/h?

9 How long does it take to travel the 335 miles from London to Cornwall at an average speed of 37 mph?

10 A 25 mile race is completed in 53 minutes by the winner. What was her average speed?

Summary of key points

Metric	Imperial
8 km	5 miles
1 kg	2.2 pounds (lb)
25 g	1 ounce (oz)
1 litre (l)	1.75 pints
4.5 l	1 gallon
1 m	39 inches
30 cm	1 foot
2.5 cm	1 inch

- $1\,m^2 = 10\,000\,cm^2$

- $1\,cm^2 = 100\,mm^2$

- $1\,m^3 = 1\,000\,000\,cm^3$

- $1\,cm^3 = 1000\,mm^3$

- **Area of a circle is given by the formula**

    $A = \pi r^2$ where A is the area
    r is the radius.

- **Circumference of a circle is given by the formula**

    $C = 2\pi r = \pi d$ where C is the circumference
    r is the radius
    d is the diameter.

- $\text{speed} = \dfrac{\text{distance}}{\text{time}}$

- $\text{average speed} = \dfrac{\text{total distance}}{\text{total time}}$

    The formula is $v = \dfrac{s}{t}$ where $v =$ speed
    $s =$ distance
    $t =$ time.

    Also: $\text{distance} = \text{speed} \times \text{time}$

    $\text{time} = \dfrac{\text{distance}}{\text{speed}}$

12 Handling data

12.1 Collecting data

■ Two-way tables can be used for discrete, continuous or grouped data.

Example 1

The incomplete table below provides some information about the numbers of shirts sold on a market stall last week:

	Small	Medium	Large	Total
White		50		120
Red	79	35	27	
Blue	40	45		139
Total	135		135	400

(a) Complete the table.

The numbers of white shirts sold is to be represented, grouped by sizes, on a pie chart.

(b) Draw the pie chart.

(a) Looking at the first column, for **Small** shirts:
The total number of **Small** shirts sold was

$$\text{White} + \text{Red} + \text{Blue} = 135$$
i.e. $\qquad \text{White} + 79 + 40 = 135$
so $\qquad\qquad \text{White} = 135 - 40 - 79$
$$\text{White} = 16$$

Then looking across the first row, for **White** shirts:

$$\text{Small} + \text{Medium} + \text{Large} = 120$$
i.e. $\qquad 16 + 50 + \text{Large} = 120$
so $\qquad\qquad \text{Large} = 120 - 50 - 16$
$$\text{Large} = 54$$

Then looking across the second row, for **Red** shirts:

$$\text{Small} + \text{Medium} + \text{Large} = \text{Total}$$
i.e. $\qquad 79 + 35 + 27 = \text{Total}$
so $\qquad\qquad \text{Total} = 141$

Then looking down the second column, for **Medium** shirts:

$$\text{Total} = \text{White} + \text{Red} + \text{Blue}$$
$$\text{Total} = 50 + 35 + 45$$
$$\text{Total} = 130$$

Then looking down the third column, for **Large** shirts:

$$White + Red + Blue = Total$$
$$54 + 27 + Blue = 135$$
$$Blue = 135 - 54 - 27$$
$$Blue = 54$$

The two-way table can be checked: the fourth column of **Totals** should add to give 400:

120 + 141 + 139 = **400** so the check is complete and correct.

The final table is:

	Small	Medium	Large	Total
White	**16**	50	**54**	120
Red	79	35	27	**141**
Blue	40	45	**54**	139
Total	135	**130**	135	400

(b) The number of white shirts sold is 120. So representing the three sizes of white shirts on a pie chart gives:

$$\text{angle for small white shirts} = \frac{16}{120} \times 360° = 48°$$

$$\text{angle for medium white shirts} = \frac{50}{120} \times 360° = 150°$$

$$\text{angle for large white shirts} = \frac{54}{120} \times 360° = 162°$$

So the pie chart is:

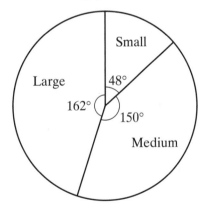

Example 2

A travel company offers three types of holiday:

    Beach   Cities   Lakes and mountains

Customers for these holidays are classified by gender as

    Male or Female

Design a two-way table which could be used to collect and record the data about the choice of holiday for people of each gender.

The appropriate table is:

	Beach	Cities	Lakes and mountains	Total
Male				
Female				
Total				

Exercise 12A   Links 16A, 16B, 23G

1   This table shows the number of jars of coffee sold in a shop last week:

(a) Complete the two-way table.

(b) How many jars were sold of:
   (i)   200 g powdered coffee
   (ii) 100 g ground coffee?

(c) Represent the total numbers of jars of ground, powder and granules sold on a pie chart.

	100 g	200 g	300 g	Total
Ground		50		100
Powder	80	40	20	
Granules	40	50		
Total	135		125	400

2   Mary is to conduct a survey into the method by which students usually travel to school.

She has identified the four methods of travel as:

    Walk   Cycle   Car   Bus

She has also classified the students as being in:

    KS3   KS4   Sixth Form

Design a two-way table Mary could use to collect and record data.

3   A group of 200 people were asked when and where they took their most recent holiday: in the UK, Europe or elsewhere. The incomplete table gives some information about their responses:

	UK	Europe	Elsewhere	Total
July		20	8	40
August	36		16	
September		32		60
Total	56	100		

(a) Complete the table.

(b) Draw a pie chart to represent the total numbers of people who went in July, August or September.

(c) Draw a second pie chart to represent the total numbers of people who went to the UK, Europe or elsewhere.

4   At the cinema they have three levels of charges. These are for Adults, Children and Senior Citizens.

They also have seats in the

Front Stalls, Rear Stalls, Front Circle and Rear Circle.

The incomplete table provides some information about the numbers of people taking various types of seat last week:

	Front Stalls	Rear Stalls	Front Circle	Rear Circle	Total
Adults	20			30	150
Children	40	32	58		140
Senior Citizens			40	60	
Total	70		178		400

Complete the table.

12.2 Representing and interpreting data

Time series

■   **A plot of values of a variable taken at regular intervals over a period of time is called a *time series*.**

■   **Points represented as a time series can be joined to create a line graph.**

Example 3
The table below shows information about the average mid-day temperatures in Malta during the summer months:

Month	April	May	June	July	August	September	October
Temperature (°C)	18	21	26	29	31	27	23

(a) Plot the points as a time series.
(b) Draw the line graph.

During the same summer months, the average mid-day temperatures in the UK are:

Month	April	May	June	July	August	September	October
Temperature (°C)	13	18	20	22	22	19	14

(c) On the same axes as for the Malta data,
   (i) plot the temperatures for the UK as a time series,
   (ii) draw the line graph for the temperatures in the UK.

(d) During which of these summer months is

(i) the average mid-day temperature in Malta at its highest?
(ii) the average mid-day temperature in the UK at its lowest?
(iii) the difference in the average mid-day temperatures in Malta and the UK at its lowest?
(iv) the difference in the average mid-day temperatures in Malta and the UK at its highest?

Mrs Jones wants to go on holiday to Malta.

She wants to go on holiday at a time when the average mid-day temperature is not above 30 °C.

She also wants to go on holiday when the difference between the average mid-day temperatures in Malta and the UK is as high as possible.

(e) During which month should Mrs Jones take her holiday in Malta?

(f) For the differences in average mid-day temperatures between Malta and the UK, work out

(i) the mean,
(ii) the median,
(iii) the mode.

(a) (b) The points plotted for the time series and the line graph for Malta are:

(c) (i) (ii)

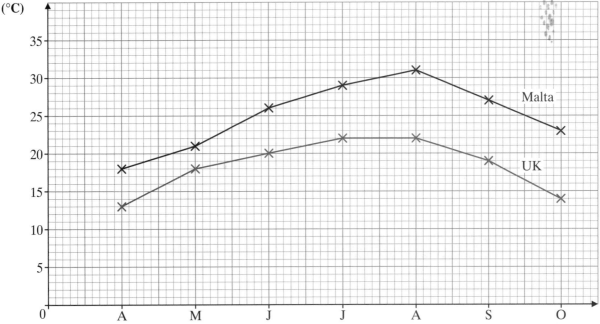

Temperature (°C)

(d) Before doing this part, it might help to redo the tables of data and include a row which shows the differences in temperature between Malta and the UK – although this information could be read off the graph.

Month	April	May	June	July	Aug	Sept	Oct
Malta temp.	18	21	26	29	31	27	23
UK temp.	13	18	20	22	22	19	14
Temp diff.	5	3	6	7	9	8	9

Now looking at either the graph or the tables we can see:

(i)   the average mid-day temperature in Malta is at its highest in August,

(ii) the average mid-day temperature in the UK is at its lowest in April,

(iii) the difference in mid-day temperatures in Malta and the UK is at its lowest in May,

(iv) the difference in mid-day temperatures in Malta and the UK is at its highest in August and October.

(e) Since Mrs Jones does not wish to go on holiday when the average mid-day temperature is above 30 degrees, this leaves October as the month when the temperature difference is at its highest. So she should go on holiday to Malta during October.

(f) The differences in average mid-day temperatures are

$$5, 3, 6, 7, 9, 8, 9$$

(i) The mean of these differences is

$$\frac{5+3+6+7+9+8+9}{7} = \frac{47}{7} = 6.71\,°\text{C (to 2 d.p.)}$$

(ii) Arrange the differences in order of size:

$$3, 5, 6, 7, 8, 9, 9$$

The median is $7\,°\text{C}$.

(iii) The mode of these differences is $9\,°\text{C}$ (9 is the number which occurs most often).

Exercise 12B   Links 10E, 10F

1   The table provides information about the average mid-day temperature in the Costa del Sol and the UK during the winter months.
All temperatures are in $°\text{C}$.

Month	Oct	Nov	Dec	Jan	Feb	Mar	Apr
Costa del Sol	24	19	17	16	17	18	21
UK	14	13	7	6	7	10	13

(a) On the same axes, plot these figures as points in time series.
(b) Draw the line graph for each time series.
(c) During which of these winter months is the difference in average mid-day temperatures in the UK and the Costa del Sol at its lowest?
(d) Work out the difference between the **means** of these average mid-day temperatures in the UK and the Costa del Sol.

2   Asif and Wendy bought their house in July 1986.
They paid £34 000 for the house.

The value of their house, in £1000s, for the next 13 years is shown in the table below:

Year	86	87	88	89	90	91	92	93	94	95	96	97	98	99
Value	34	37	40	33	31	31	32	33	34	38	40	44	53	64

(a) Plot this data as points in a time series.
(b) Draw the line graph for this time series.
(c) Make **four** comments about how the value of Asif and Wendy's house varied between 1986 and 1999.

3   Mrs Sharma pays her gas bill in March, June, August and
December each year.

The table below provides information about her gas bills for
the years 1999 to 2001:

	March	June	August	December
1999	£268	£182	£121	£206
2000	£284	£191	£128	£217
2001	£301	£199	£140	£230

(a)   Represent this information graphically as a time series.
(b)   Draw the line graph for the time series.
(c)   Make three statistical comments about how Mrs Sharma's
gas bill varied from March 1999 to December 2001.

Retail Price Index

■   **The Retail Price Index measures how prices change over a period of time.**

The Retail Price Index was set at 100 in January 1987. To do this
the government chose some household goods we all buy, such as
bread, milk, and so on, and worked out their combined prices and
set this as 100. So when we are told that the Retail Price Index in
November 2001 is 173.6 it means that the price of these basic
goods has gone up by a factor of 1.736.

The factor or ratio is

$$\frac{173.6}{100} = 1.736$$

In other words, what you could buy for £100 in January 1987 would
cost £173.60 in November 2001.

The table below provides a full list of the Retail Price Index from
January 1987 up to November 2001:

1987	100.0	100.4	100.6	101.8	101.9	101.9	101.8	102.1	102.4	102.9	103.4	103.3
1988	103.3	103.7	104.1	105.8	106.2	106.6	106.7	107.9	108.4	109.5	110.0	110.3
1989	111.0	111.8	112.3	114.3	115.0	115.4	115.5	115.8	116.6	117.5	118.5	118.8
1990	119.5	120.2	121.4	125.1	126.2	126.7	126.8	128.1	129.3	130.3	130.0	129.9
1991	130.2	130.9	131.4	133.1	133.5	134.1	133.8	134.1	134.6	135.1	135.6	135.7
1992	135.6	136.3	136.7	138.8	139.3	139.3	138.8	138.9	139.4	139.9	139.7	139.2
1993	137.9	138.8	139.3	140.6	141.1	141.0	140.7	141.3	141.9	141.8	141.6	141.9
1994	141.3	142.1	142.5	144.2	144.7	144.7	144.0	144.7	145.0	145.2	145.3	146.0
1995	146.0	146.9	147.5	149.0	149.6	149.8	149.1	149.9	150.6	149.8	149.8	150.7
1996	150.2	150.9	151.5	152.6	152.9	153.0	152.4	153.1	153.8	153.8	153.9	154.4
1997	154.4	155.0	155.4	156.3	156.9	157.5	157.5	158.5	159.3	159.5	159.6	160.0
1998	159.5	160.3	160.8	162.6	163.5	163.4	163.0	163.7	164.4	164.5	164.4	164.4
1999	163.4	163.7	164.1	165.2	165.6	165.6	165.1	165.5	166.2	166.5	166.7	167.3
2000	166.6	167.5	168.4	170.1	170.7	171.1	170.5	170.5	171.7	171.6	172.1	172.2
2001	171.1	172.0	172.2	173.1	174.2	174.4	173.3	174.0	174.6	174.3	173.6	

Example 4

Workwell is a small company.
It is company policy to keep wages in line with changes in the
Retail Price Index (RPI).

Sam joined Workwell on 1st January 1987.
His weekly wage then was exactly £100.
For the next 14 years he stayed at Workwell doing the same job.
Work out what Sam's weekly wage would have been
(a) during January 1997
(b) during January 2001.

(a) In January 1987, the RPI was 100.
In January 1997, the RPI was 154.4.
So the proportional change (or factor) in the RPI

$$= \frac{154.4}{100} = 1.544.$$

So to keep in line with the changes in RPI, Sam's wage in
January 1997 would have been

wage in January 1987 × proportional change in RPI
$$= £100 \times 1.544 = £154.40$$

(b) In January 2001 the RPI was 171.1.
So the proportional change in RPI between January 1987

and January 2001 was $\frac{171.1}{100} = 1.711.$

So to keep in line with changes in the RPI, Sam's wage in
January 2001 would have been

$$£100 \times 1.711 = £171.10$$

Example 5

The table below provides information about the Retail Price Index
in the UK and in Malta from January 1995 to January 2001:

Year	1995	1996	1997	1998	1999	2000	2001
RPI (UK)	146.0	150.2	154.4	159.5	163.4	166.6	171.1
RPI (Malta)	100	99.87	103.57	107.10	108.62	112.24	112.95

(a) On the same axes, plot both sets of RPIs as points in a time
series and draw their respective line graphs.
(b) Plot the RPI in Malta against the RPI in the UK as points on
a scatter diagram.
(c) On your scatter diagram draw the line of best fit.
(d) Comment on the correlation between the RPI in Malta and
the RPI in the UK.

The local newspaper in Malta claimed that price rises on the island between 1995 and 2001 had been lower than price rises in the UK over the same period.

(e) Comment on the newspaper's claim.

(a)

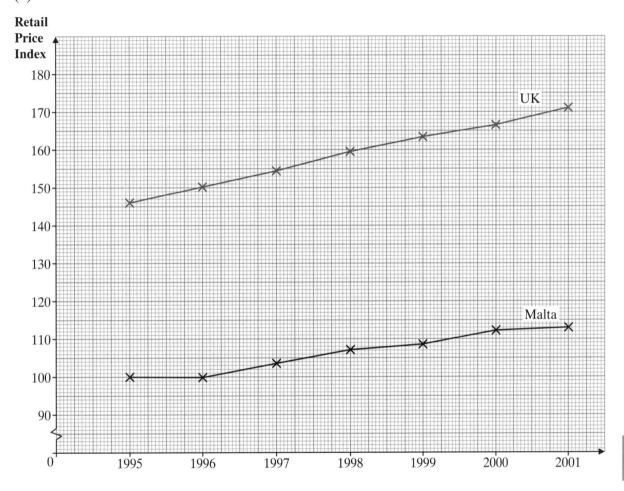

(b) (c)

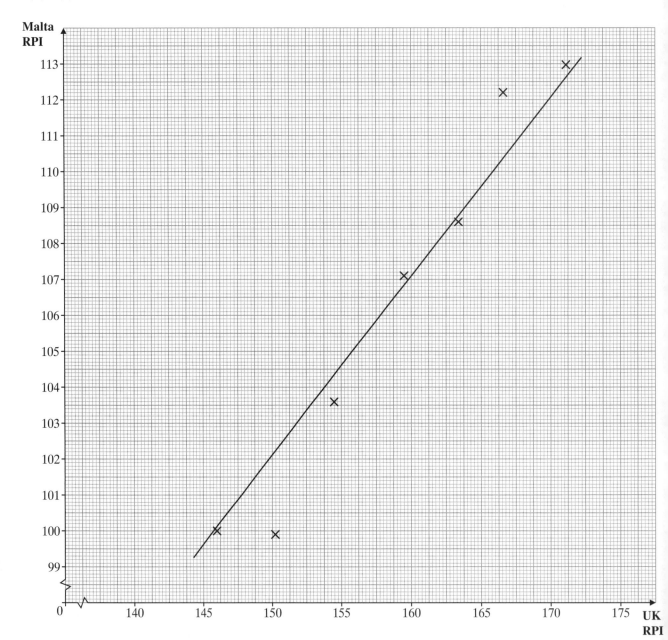

(d) The scatter diagram shows **positive correlation** between the
RPI in the UK and the RPI in Malta.

(e) Between 1995 and 2001 the proportional changes in RPI have
been:

$$\text{For UK: } \frac{171.1}{146.0} = 1.1719 \qquad \text{For Malta: } \frac{112.95}{100} = 1.1295$$

The change in RPI for the UK is greater than the change in
RPI for Malta over the period from 1995 to 2001.
This indicates that the newspaper's claim is correct.

Exercise 12C   Links

1   Asif joined Wellworkers Ltd in August 1996.
    His salary was then £12 500 per year.
    The RPI in August 1996 was 153.1.
    In August 2001 the RPI was 174.0.
    Between August 1996 and August 2001, Asif received salary
    increases which were in line with changes in the RPI.
    Work out Asif's salary in August 2001.

2   In January 1975 the RPI was 30.39.
    In January 2000 the RPI was 166.6.
    In January 1975 the price of a loaf of bread was 12p.
    Assuming that bread prices follow the changes in the RPI,
    work out the price of a similar loaf of bread in January 2001.

3   In December 2000 the RPI was 172.2.
    In December 1960 the RPI was 12.62.
    The price of a loaf of bread was 62p in December 2000.
    Stating your assumptions, work out an estimate of the price of
    a similar loaf of bread in December 1960.

4   The table below provides information about the Retail Price
    Index in the UK and on the island of Guernsey during the
    months of September from 1994 to 2001:

	1994	1995	1996	1997	1998	1999	2000	2001
UK	145.0	150.6	153.8	159.3	164.4	166.2	171.7	174.6
Guernsey	100.2	104.2	106.2	110.9	115.4	117.4	122.7	125.9

(a) On the same axes:
   (i) plot each set of Retail Price Indices as a time series,
   (ii) draw the line graphs.

(b) Plot the two sets of data as points on a scatter diagram.

(c) Draw the line of best fit on the scatter diagram.

(d) Comment on the relationship between the RPI in the UK
    and the RPI on Guernsey.

A local radio station on Guernsey claims that during the years
from 1994 to 2001 the price rises on the island have been
lower than those on the mainland UK.

(e) Explain whether the table of RPIs provides evidence to
    support this claim or not.

Other social statistics

■ **The government keeps many forms of statistic relevant to our lives.**

These figures include:

- the number of babies born each year
- the number of people unemployed in each month
- the number of marriages each year
- the number of road accidents each week
- pass rates in GCSE examinations
- monthly inflation rates
- the National Census.

Example 6

The government made an estimation of the distribution of the overall population of the United Kingdom in the middle of the year 2000.
The results of this exercise are shown in the table below:

| Mid-2000 UK population estimates ||
UK countries	Population estimates
United Kingdom	59 755 700
England	49 997 100
Wales	2 946 200
Scotland	5 114 600
Northern Ireland	1 697 800

(a) Draw a bar chart to show the numbers of people living in England, Northern Ireland, Scotland and Wales.
(b) Use the data to work out an estimate of the percentage of the UK population living in Scotland.

(a) The appropriate bar chart is as below:

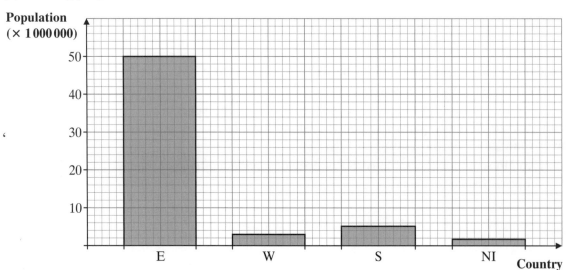

(b) The percentage of the UK population living in Scotland is

$$\frac{5\,114\,600}{59\,755\,700} \times 100 = 8.6\% \text{ to one place of decimals}$$

Exercise 12D   Links

1   The government's estimate of the population of England in
    mid-2000 was 49 997 100.
    It was estimated that the distribution of this population by
    region was as given in the table below:

English regions	Population estimates
North East	2 577 300
North West	6 893 900
Yorkshire and Humber	5 057 900
East Midlands	4 207 900
West Midlands	5 335 400
East Anglia	5 459 600
London	7 375 100
South East	8 114 900
South West	4 975 100

(a) Represent this data on a bar chart.
(b) Represent this data on a pie chart.
(c) As far as the population of England is concerned, which is
    the **modal** region?

The average price of a house in each of these English regions
in the year 2000 is given in the table below:

North East	£52 500
North West	£65 000
Yorkshire and Humber	£61 000
East Midlands	£68 850
West Midlands	£76 200
East Anglia	£82 500
London	£147 500
South East	£120 000
South West	£88 800

(d) Write these average prices in order, starting with the smallest.
(e) Draw a scatter diagram for the average price of a house against the population.
(f) Draw a line of best fit on your scatter diagram.
(g) Comment on the relationship between house prices and population.

2   The table below provides information about the Year 2000 census figures from the USA:

Age range	Number of people	% of population
Under 5 years	19 175 798	6.8
5 to 9 years	20 549 505	7.3
10 to 14 years	20 528 072	7.3
15 to 19 years	20 219 890	7.2
20 to 24 years	18 964 001	6.7
25 to 34 years	39 891 724	14.2
35 to 44 years	45 148 527	16.0
45 to 54 years	37 677 952	13.4
55 to 59 years	13 469 237	4.8
60 to 64 years	10 805 447	3.8
65 to 74 years	18 390 986	6.5
75 to 84 years	12 361 180	4.4
85 years and over	4 239 587	1.5

(a) Round the population number for each age group
  (i) correct to the nearest million,
  (ii) correct to the nearest hundred thousand.
(b) Using your rounded figures in (i) above, draw a histogram of the population for each age group.
(c) Write down the modal class interval for the age group.

3   The table below shows the pass rates (as percentages) for GCSE English in summer 2000 and summer 2001 at Lucea High School:

	A*	A	B	C	D	E	F	G	U
2000	3%	12%	21%	24%	18%	17%	3%	2%	0
2001	2.8%	13.2%	23%	22%	17%	16%	3%	3%	0

Make three valid comments about these pass rates.

4   During the summer of 2002, 32 countries took part in the finals of the football World Cup.
Correct to the nearest million and in millions, the populations of those countries at the time of the World Cup were as follows:

38	10	176	16	1348	4	4	5
13	59	82	4	58	127	49	100
147	5	10	142	22	10	2	45
41	9	10	70	60	287	3	39

(a) Which of these population figures could be described as *exceptional*? Give your reasons.

(b) Explain whether the **mean**, **mode** or **median** would truly reflect the average population of a country taking part in the World Cup finals.

(c) Represent the population figures on a **stem and leaf** diagram.

The first World Cup final took place in 1930. The table below shows the countries that have subsequently won the World Cup, the number of times each country has won it and the population (in millions) of each country:

Country	Number of wins	Population
Brazil	4	176
Italy	3	58
Germany	3	82
Argentina	2	38
Uruguay	2	3
England	1	60
France	1	59

(d) Explain why this data gives the people of Uruguay every right to feel proud of their country's achievement in the World Cup.

Summary of key points

- Two-way tables can be used for discrete, continuous or grouped data.

- A plot of values of a variable taken at regular intervals over a period of time is called a *time series*.

- Points represented as a time series can be joined to create a line graph.

- The Retail Price Index measures how prices change over a period of time.

- The government keeps many forms of statistic relevant to our lives.

13 Probability

13.1 Probability

Teaching reference:
pp 355–370,
sections 23.1–23.7

- Probability is a measure of the chance that some event will happen.

- An event which is certain to happen has a probability of 1.

- An event which cannot happen has a probability of 0.

- The probability that an event will happen is

$$\text{probability} = \frac{\text{number of successful outcomes}}{\text{total number of possible outcomes}}$$

  assuming all outcomes are equally likely.

- The probability of an event happening is always greater than or equal to 0 (impossible) and less than or equal to 1 (certain). This can be written as

$$0 \leqslant \text{probability} \leqslant 1$$

- Probability must be expressed as a fraction, decimal or percentage.

- When an event has different mutually exclusive outcomes (*mutually exclusive* means that if one happens then another cannot happen) then the sum of the probabilities of these outcomes is 1.

- If the probability of an event happening is p, then the probability of it not happening is $1 - p$.

- The estimated probability that an event will happen in a game or experiment is

$$\text{estimated probability} = \frac{\text{number of successful trials}}{\text{total number of trials}}$$

  The estimated probability is sometimes called the *relative frequency* that the event will happen.

- Sample space diagrams and two-way tables can be used to help solve probability problems.

Example 1

Sandy has a bag of 15 chocolates: 8 plain, 5 milk and 2 white.

She selects a chocolate at random from the bag.

(a) Which type of chocolate is it most likely to be?
(b) Write down the probability that she will select a milk chocolate.
(c) Write down the probability that she will select a chocolate which is either milk or white.
(d) Write down the probability that she will select a chocolate which is **not** white.
(e) Write down the probability that she will select a sugared almond.

(a) There are more plain chocolates than any other chocolates in the bag. So the chocolate she selects is most likely to be plain.

(b) There are 5 milk chocolates out of a total of 15. So

$$\text{probability(milk)} = \frac{5}{15}$$

You could cancel this to $\frac{1}{3}$ but there is no need to do so unless it is specifically required by the question.

(c) There are 5 milk and 2 white for a total of 7, so

$$\text{probability(milk or white)} = \frac{7}{15}$$

(d) Probability(not white) = 1 − probability(white)

$$= 1 - \frac{2}{15}$$

$$= \frac{13}{15}$$

(e) There are no sugared almonds in the bag, so it is impossible to select one. Therefore

$$\text{probability(sugared almond)} = 0$$

Example 2

The diagram represents a biased spinner in the shape of a pentagon. When the spinner is spun once, the probability of it stopping on each of the sections A to D is given in the table:

Section	A	B	C	D	E
Probability	0.23	0.14	0.18	0.26	

Work out the probability that the spinner will stop on section E.

The sum of the probabilities must be 1. So

$$0.23 + 0.14 + 0.18 + 0.26 + \text{probability(E)} = 1$$
$$0.81 + \text{probability(E)} = 1$$
$$\text{probability(E)} = 1 - 0.81$$
$$\text{probability(E)} = 0.19$$

So the probability of it landing on section E is 0.19.

Example 3

The probability of a new computer being faulty is 0.002.

(a) Work out the probability of a new computer **not** being faulty.

A computer retail company takes a stock of 12 000 new computers.

(b) Work out an estimate of the number of these new computers likely to be faulty.

(a) Probability(not faulty) $= 1 -$ probability(faulty)
$$= 1 - 0.002$$
$$= 0.998$$

(b) Probability of being faulty is 0.002 (i.e. 2 out of every 1000 will be faulty).
So the likely number of faulty computers out of a batch of 12 000 is

$$0.002 \times 12\,000 = 24$$

Example 4

Andy has a biased spinner in the shape of a pentagon.
He conducts an experiment to work out estimates for the probability of the spinner stopping on each of the five sections.

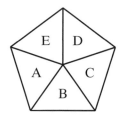

A the end of his experiment, he has made the estimates for the five probabilities as given in the table below:

Section	A	B	C	D	E
Probability	0.23	0.22	0.17	0.24	0.21

Explain why Andy must have a made a mistake.

The sum of Andy's probabilities is

$$0.23 + 0.22 + 0.17 + 0.24 + 0.21 = 1.07$$

But the sum of the probabilities cannot be greater than 1. Hence Andy must have made a mistake.

Example 5

There are four candidates in an election. Their names are

Addison, Bywaters, Cambell and Davis.

Shortly before the election, a market research company conduct a survey of 1200 people in which they ask voters for which candidate they intend to vote. The results of this survey are as follows:

Name of candidate	Addison	Bywaters	Cambell	Davis
Frequency	340	540	204	116

On the day of the election, a voter is chosen at random. Work out the best estimate of the probability of that voter voting for Bywaters.

The survey suggests that 540 out of 1200 voters will vote for Bywaters.
Hence the best estimate of the probability of a randomly chosen voter voting for Bywaters is

$$\frac{540}{1200} = \frac{54}{120} = \frac{9}{20} \text{ or } 0.45 \text{ or } 45\%$$

Any of these answers is acceptable.

Example 6

The diagram represents a fair coin and a fair spinner.
The spinner is in the shape of an equilateral triangle.

Asif will toss the coin once and spin the
spinner once. He will record the joint outcomes on
a sample space diagram.

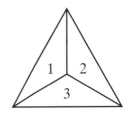

(a) Construct the sample space diagram.
(b) Work out the probability of the joint outcome Heads and a
    number less than 3.

(a) The sample space diagram is:

```
3        •        •
       (H, 3)  (T, 3)

2        •        •
       (H, 2)  (T, 2)

1        •        •
       (H, 1)  (T, 1)

         H        T
```

(b) We need the joint outcome of Heads and a number less than
    3, so the 'successful' outcomes are

     (H, 1)   (H, 2)

From the sample space diagram, there are 6 joint outcomes in
total.
Of these 6, only 2 are 'successful', i.e. consist of a Head and a
number less than 3.

So probability (H and no. < 3) $= \dfrac{2}{6}$ or $\dfrac{1}{3}$

Exercise 13A

1   A bag contains 20 coloured snooker balls.
     9 of the balls are red, 6 are blue, 3 are white and 2 are black.
     A ball is to be selected at random from the bag.
     (a) Which colour is the ball selected least likely to be?
         Give your reasoning.
     (b) Write down the probability of the selected ball being blue.
     (c) Work out the probability of the selected ball being:
         (i) blue or black   **(ii)** red, white or black
         (iii) not red   **(iv)** green.

2   The probability of a newly laid egg being cracked is 0.002.
   (a) Work out the probability of a newly laid egg **not** being
        cracked.
   A supermarket took delivery of 140 000 newly laid eggs.
   (b) Work out, showing all of your reasoning, the most likely
        number of eggs out of the 140 000 to be cracked.

3   The probability of a train being late is $\frac{1}{15}$.
   Work out the probability of the train **not** being late.

4   The school bus can be **late**, **on time** or **early**.
   The probability of it being late is 0.26.
   The probability of it being on time is 0.65.
   Work out the probability of the school bus being early.

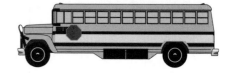

5   The diagram represents a cubical dice. The dice is biased.
   When it is rolled once, the probabilities of it showing each of
   the numbers from 1 to 5 on its uppermost face are given in the
   incomplete table below:

Number	1	2	3	4	5	6
Probability	0.12	0.21	0.17	0.15	0.14	

   Work out the probability of the dice showing a six on its
   uppermost face when it is rolled once.

6   The probability of the school bus being late is estimated to
   be 15%. During the year the school bus makes 195 journeys
   to the school.
   Work out an estimate for the most likely number of times
   the school bus will be late during the year.

7   The diagram represents two fair spinners:
   One spinner has three sections labelled 1, 2 and 3.
   The other spinner has four sections labelled 1, 2, 3 and 4.
   Each spinner is spun once and the joint outcome recorded.
   (a) Draw a sample space for the joint outcomes.
   (b) Find the probability of the joint outcome

             first spinner stops on 3 and second spinner stops on 4.

   The numbers on the two sections that the spinners land on are
   added to give a total score.
   (c) Work out the probability of obtaining a total score
       (i)   of 4
       (ii) which is an even number
       (iii) which is an odd number.

8 James writes books. The probability of him spelling a word incorrectly is 0.003.
James wrote a book of 120 000 words. Work out an estimate of the most likely number of words in this book to be spelt incorrectly.

Summary of key points

■ Probability is a measure of the chance that some event will happen.

■ An event which is certain to happen has a probability of 1.

■ An event which cannot happen has a probability of 0.

■ The probability that an event will happen is

$$\text{probability} = \frac{\text{number of successful outcomes}}{\text{total number of possible outcomes}}$$

assuming all outcomes are equally likely.

■ The probability of an event happening is always greater than or equal to 0 (impossible) and less than or equal to 1 (certain).
This can be written as

$$0 \leqslant \text{probability} \leqslant 1$$

■ Probability must be expressed as a fraction, decimal or percentage.

■ When an event has different mutually exclusive outcomes (*mutually exclusive* means that if one happens then another cannot happen) then the sum of the probabilities of these outcomes is 1.

■ If the probability of an event happening is p, then the probability of it not happening is $1 - p$.

■ The estimated probability that an event will happen in a game or experiment is

$$\text{estimated probability} = \frac{\text{number of successful trials}}{\text{total number of trials}}$$

The estimated probability is sometimes called the *relative frequency* that the event will happen.

■ Sample space diagrams and two-way tables can be used to help solve probability problems.

Terminal practice paper 1

You must not use a calculator.

1 (a) Work out $161 \div 7$. (1)

(b) Work out $526 - 274$. (2)

(c) Write down the value of the 4 in the number 8419. (1)

2 (a) Write down the fraction of this shape which is shaded. Give your answer in its simplest form. (2)

(b) Write your answer to part (a) as a percentage. (1)

3 Here are the first three shapes in a sequence of shapes made from matchsticks:

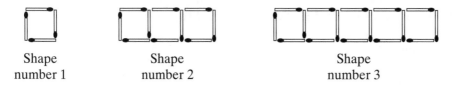

| Shape number 1 | Shape number 2 | Shape number 3 |

(a) Draw shape number 4. (1)

(b) Complete the table:

Shape number	1	2	3	4	5
Number of matchsticks	4	10	16		

(1)

(c) Work out the number of matchsticks in shape number 11. (2)

(d) Explain why no shape in this sequence will have 365 matchsticks in it. (1)

4 Write down the mathematical name of each of these solids:

(a) (b) (c)

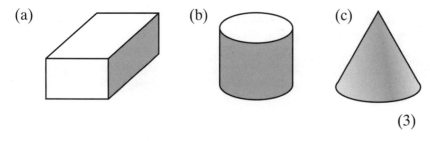

(3)

5 (a) Work out an estimate for the value of 3.7×53. (2)

(b) Work out an estimate for the value of $\sqrt{50}$. (1)

6 Write down the **imperial** unit you would use to measure:
   (a) the weight of a baby
   (b) the volume of water in a pond
   (c) the diameter of a pizza.   (3)

7 This word formula can be used to work out the roasting time, in minutes, for a duck:

   roasting time = 25 × (weight in pounds + 1)

   (a) Work out the roasting time for a duck which weighs 6 pounds.   (2)
   The roasting time for a duck which weighs w pounds is T minutes.
   (b) Write down a formula for T in terms of w.   (2)

8 Paul carried out a survey of the blood groups of the students in his class. He recorded the results like this:

A	A	B	O	AB	O	A	A	O	A
O	B	AB	A	O	O	O	A	O	A
A	O	O	A	B	A	O	O	A	O

   Use a better method to record the results.   (3)

9 (a) Work out $\frac{7}{8}$ of £56.   (2)
   (b) Work out 8% of 700.   (2)

10 The table shows the number, in millions, of mobile phone users in the UK every two years from 1990 to 2000:

Year	1990	1992	1994	1996	1998	2000	2002
Number of mobile phone users in the UK (million)	1	2	3	7	13	24	

   (a) Draw a time series line graph to illustrate the data.   (2)
   (b) Use your graph to find an estimate for the number of mobile phone users in the UK in 1999.   (1)
   (c) Use your graph to make a prediction for the number of mobile phone users in the UK in 2002.   (1)

11

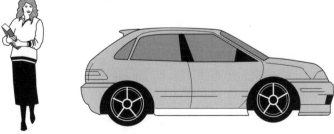

The diagram shows a car and a woman of average height.
Find an estimate for the length of the car.
Explain clearly how you obtained your answer.   (4)

12 1 cm^3 of tin weighs 7.31 g.
   (a) Work out the weight of 25 cm^3 of tin.   (3)
   Gunmetal contains copper and tin in the ratio 4 : 1.
   (b) Work out the weight of copper in 35 kg of gunmetal.   (2)

13 *A* has coordinates (1, 4). *B* has coordinates (3, 1).
   C has coordinates (7, 4). *ABCD* is a kite.
   (a) Find the coordinates of *D*.   (2)
   (b) Find the coordinates of the mid-point of the line segment
        AD.   (2)

14 (a) Work out $\frac{3}{4} \times \frac{2}{5}$.   (2)

   (b) Work out $\frac{3}{4} - \frac{2}{5}$.   (2)

15 (a) Convert 56 km to miles.   (2)
   (b) Convert 6.7 m^2 to cm^2.   (2)

16 The table shows the probability that a set of traffic lights will
   be red, red with amber, or green:

Colours	red	red with amber	green	amber
Probability	0.34	0.01	0.62	

   Amber is the only other colour that a set of traffic lights can
   be. Work out the probability that the set of traffic lights will be
   amber.   (2)

17 Solve $x - 4 = 2 - 3x$.   (3)

Terminal practice paper 2

You may use a calculator.

1 A bottle of lemonade costs 35p.
   Rachel buys 4 bottles of lemonade.
   She pays with a £5 note.
   (a) How much change should she receive?   (3)
   A bottle of cola costs 43p.
   Graham has £5.
   (b) What is the greatest number of bottles of cola he can
        buy?   (2)

2 The rule for a sequence is **multiply the previous term by 4**.
   48 is a term of the sequence.
   (a) Work out the next term after 48.   (1)
   (b) Work out the term immediately before 48.   (2)

3 'The lengths of the sides of a particular quadrilateral are
   equal.'
   (a) Sketch **two** quadrilaterals which fit this description. (2)
   (b) Write down the mathematical name of each of these
        quadrilaterals.   (2)

4 The table shows the costs, in 2001, of sending items with a
   weight of up to 500 g by first class and second class post:

Weight up to	First class	Second class
60 g	27p	19p
100 g	41p	33p
150 g	57p	44p
200 g	72p	54p
250 g	84p	66p
300 g	96p	76p
350 g	£1.09	87p
400 g	£1.24	£1.00
450 g	£1.41	£1.14
500 g	£1.58	£1.30

A letter weighs 320 g.
(a) Write down the cost of sending it by first class post.   (1)
4 letters each weigh 180 g. They are sent by second class post.
(b) Work out the total cost of sending the 4 letters.   (2)
Kylie sent a package by second class post.
It would have cost her 27p more to send it by first class post.
(c) Find the greatest possible weight of her package.   (2)

5 This graph can be used to convert between pounds (£) and New Zealand dollars:

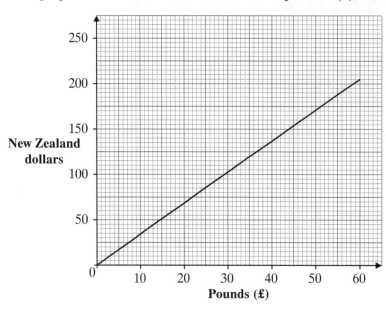

(a) Use the graph to convert:
  (i) £34 to New Zealand dollars
  (ii) 65 New Zealand dollars to pounds. (2)
(b) Convert £200 to New Zealand dollars. Explain clearly how you obtained your answer. (2)

6 One night last winter, the temperature in London was 2 °C,
  in Leeds was −3 °C
  and in Glasgow was −9 °C.
(a) Work out the difference in temperature between London and Glasgow. (1)
The temperature in Swansea was 8 °C higher than the temperature in Leeds.
(b) Work out the temperature in Swansea. (1)
The temperature in Dundee was 4 °C lower than the temperature in Glasgow.
(c) Work out the temperature in Dundee. (1)

7 The table shows, for certain loans, the monthly repayments, in £, and the number of months over which the loan is repaid:

		Number of months				
		12	24	36	48	60
	2000	187.96	104.55	77.21	63.88	56.15
	3000	281.94	156.82	115.82	95.83	84.23
Amount borrowed (£)	4000	375.92	209.10	154.40	127.77	112.30
	5000	469.90	261.37	193.00	159.71	140.38
	6000	563.88	313.64	231.64	191.66	168.46

Gordon borrowed £4000 and repaid the loan over 48 months.
(a) (i)   Write down his monthly repayment.
    (ii) How much more did Gordon repay than he
          borrowed?
    (iii) Express your answer to part (ii) as a percentage of
          £4000.   (6)
Julie borrowed £5000 and her monthly repayment was £140.38.
(b) Over how many months did Julie repay the loan?   (1)
Leroy made 36 monthly repayments of £115.82.
(c) How much did Leroy borrow?   (1)

8 Find $4.7^3 - \sqrt{51.84}$.   (2)

9 (a) Solve $3x + 7 = 1$.   (2)
       (b) Expand $5(y - 4)$.   (1)
       (c) Factorize $t^2 - 6t$.   (2)

10 The diagram shows a parallelogram.
        (a) Write down:
             (i)   the number of lines of
                   symmetry it has
             (ii) its order of rotational symmetry. (2)
        (b) (i)   Measure the size of the angle
                   marked x.
             (ii) Write down the special name
                   for this type of angle.   (2)

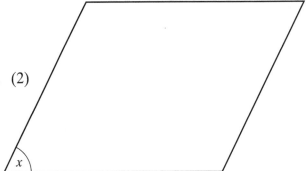

11 6 five pence pieces weigh 19.5 grams.
        Work out the weight of 11 five pence pieces.   (3)

12 The diagram shows a solid shape made from cubes.
        The length of every edge of each cube is 1 cm.

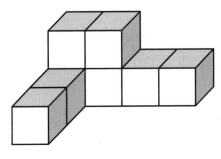

Diagram NOT
accurately drawn.

(a) Find the volume of the solid shape.   (2)
(b) Make an accurate drawing of the plan of the solid. (2)

13 Here are the weights, in kilograms, of 10 men:

76   63   81   68   94   87   90   68   78   85

Work out the mean weight of the men.   (3)

14 In triangle *DEF*, *DE* = 7.2 cm, *DF* = 6.3 cm and *EF* = 5.7 cm.
Make an accurate drawing of triangle *DEF*.
Show all your construction lines.   (2)

15 (a)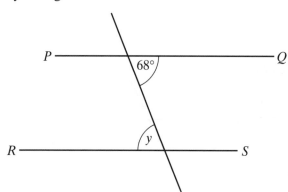

Diagram NOT
accurately drawn.

Explain why triangle *ABC* is isosceles.   (2)

(b)

Diagram NOT
accurately drawn.

PQ is parallel to *RS*.
Explain why *y* = 68°.   (1)

16 The index numbers in the table give information about average
house prices between 1991 and 1997:

1991	1992	1993	1994	1995	1996	1997
100	99	96	97	102	101	108

(a) How did house prices in 1994 compare with those in
1991?   (2)

In 1991, Jenny bought a house for £85 000.
She sold it in 1997.
The price of her house had changed by the same percentage as
average house prices between 1991 and 1997.
(b) Work out the price for which Jenny sold her house.   (2)

Answers

Exercise 1A

1 (a) $\frac{3}{5}$ (b) $\frac{5}{7}$ (c) $\frac{2}{3}$ (d) $\frac{1}{4}$ (e) $\frac{2}{5}$
   (f) $\frac{1}{3}$ (g) $1\frac{1}{5}$ (h) $1\frac{2}{3}$ (i) $1\frac{1}{5}$ (j) 1

2 (a) $1\frac{1}{4}$ (b) $1\frac{3}{8}$ (c) $1\frac{1}{2}$
   (d) $\frac{1}{4}$ (e) $\frac{1}{2}$ (f) $\frac{1}{4}$
   (g) $\frac{11}{12}$ (h) $1\frac{3}{20}$ (i) $\frac{23}{24}$
   (j) $\frac{5}{12}$ (k) $\frac{2}{15}$ (l) $\frac{27}{40}$
   (m) $\frac{41}{60}$ (n) $\frac{69}{77}$ (o) $1\frac{31}{52}$
   (p) $\frac{26}{63}$ (q) $\frac{14}{65}$ (r) $\frac{7}{60}$

3 (a) 4 (b) $5\frac{4}{5}$ (c) $5\frac{5}{7}$
   (d) $3\frac{1}{4}$ (e) $3\frac{1}{2}$ (f) $1\frac{2}{8}$
   (g) $6\frac{3}{4}$ (h) $3\frac{7}{10}$ (i) $1\frac{3}{8}$
   (j) $3\frac{1}{15}$ (k) $3\frac{26}{35}$ (l) $4\frac{20}{21}$
   (m) $2\frac{4}{21}$ (n) $3\frac{19}{40}$

4 $1\frac{1}{4}$ kg
5 $2\frac{7}{8}$ yards
6 (a) $\frac{17}{30}$ (b) $\frac{13}{30}$
7 $1\frac{1}{8}$ kg
8 $2\frac{1}{8}$ yards
9 3 hours
10 $2\frac{1}{4}$ hours

Exercise 1B

1 (a) $\frac{1}{5}$ (b) $\frac{2}{7}$
   (c) $\frac{5}{16}$ (d) $\frac{1}{14}$
   (e) $\frac{3}{20}$ (f) $\frac{4}{15}$
   (g) $\frac{7}{96}$ (h) $\frac{9}{40}$
   (i) $\frac{1}{27}$ (j) $\frac{1}{14}$

2 $\frac{3}{20}$
3 $\frac{1}{4}$ kg
4 $\frac{1}{4}$ hour
5 $\frac{5}{8}$ yards

Exercise 1C

1 $\frac{2}{5}$ 2 $\frac{2}{5}$ 3 $\frac{1}{4}$
4 $\frac{3}{25}$ 5 $\frac{5}{7}$ 6 $\frac{3}{7}$
7 $\frac{4}{9}$ 8 $\frac{1}{2}$ 9 $\frac{2}{15}$
10 $\frac{2}{11}$ 11 $\frac{2}{25}$ 12 $\frac{3}{19}$

Exercise 1D

1 (a) $\frac{5}{7}$ (b) $\frac{3}{11}$ (c) $1\frac{1}{2}$ (d) $\frac{1}{3}$
2 (a) $1\frac{7}{15}$ (b) $\frac{7}{20}$ (c) $\frac{3}{8}$ (d) $1\frac{1}{10}$
3 (a) $5\frac{5}{8}$ (b) $3\frac{11}{20}$ (c) $3\frac{9}{10}$ (d) $2\frac{7}{30}$
4 $3\frac{3}{4}$ kg
5 $1\frac{1}{8}$ yards
6 (a) $\frac{2}{9}$ (b) $\frac{2}{5}$
   (c) $\frac{7}{32}$ (d) $\frac{2}{15}$
7 $\frac{5}{24}$
8 (a) $\frac{1}{2}$ (b) $\frac{2}{3}$
   (c) $\frac{5}{48}$ (d) $\frac{1}{2}$

Exercise 2A

1 (a) 30 (b) 330 (c) 500 (d) 2800
   (e) 3000 (f) 5000 (g) 5820 (h) 500
2 (a) 300 (b) 5000 (c) 300 (d) 40
   (e) 5000 (f) 70 000 (g) 30 (h) 30 000
3 (a) 5 (b) 2 (c) 8 (d) 7
   (e) 9 (f) 10 (g) 2 (h) 3
4 (a) 0.3 (b) 0.7 (c) 0.08 (d) 0.06
   (e) 0.003 (f) 0.003 (g) 0.08 (h) 1.0
5 1000 6 30 000 7 £20 000

Exercise 2B

1 (a) (i) 400×40 (ii) 16 000
   (b) (i) $1000 \div 40$ (ii) 25
   (c) (i) $\frac{800 \times 5000}{3000}$ (ii) $1333\frac{1}{3}$
   (d) (i) 600×3 (ii) 1800
   (e) (i) $400 \div 5$ (ii) 80
   (f) (i) 7×2 (ii) 14
   (g) (i) $9 \div 2$ (ii) 4.5
   (h) (i) $\frac{4 \times 5}{10}$ (ii) 2
   (i) (i) $\frac{2 \times 8}{4 \times 2}$ (ii) 2

2 (a) (i) 15 709 (ii) $700 \times 20 = 14\,000$
   (b) (i) 126.9 (ii) $50 \times 3 = 150$
   (c) (i) 29.14 (ii) $3 \times 9 = 27$
   (d) (i) 11 (ii) $400 \div 40 = 10$
   (e) (i) 39 (ii) $300 \div 9 = 33\frac{1}{3}$
   (f) (i) 3 (ii) $10 \div 3 = 3\frac{1}{3}$
   (g) (i) 7.76 (3 s.f.) (ii) $\frac{900 \div 20}{5} = 9$
   (h) (i) 0.362 (3 s.f.) (ii) $\frac{3 \times 3}{20} = 0.45$

Exercise 2C

1 £13.09
2 15 packs
3 9 egg boxes
4 £6.66
5 £5.62
6 42 g
7 It is not possible to measure 9.554 cm; 9.6 cm is more sensible.
8 Shoe sizes are only in whole or half sizes.
9 16 cars
10 He cannot be paid exactly £21.333 33 (£21.33 is more sensible)

Exercise 2D

1 (a) £30 (b) £5.70
   (c) £6.13 (d) £30
   (e) £7920 (f) £4.63 (to nearest penny)
2 (a) £780 (b) £16 380
3 £16 740
4 Sofa – £315, Bed – £139.30, Coffee table – £21.35
5 (a) £16.71 (b) £3.14 (c) £1373.75
6 £206.25
7 €8
8 (a) £0.93 (b) £52.43
9 £113.70
10 (a) £19 440 (b) £188
    (c) £17 560 (d) £4051.20

Exercise 2E

1 (a) 30   (b) 50   (c) 200
   (d) 6000   (e) 4   (f) 0.02
2 20 000 people
3 (a) (i) 400×50 (ii) 20 000
   (b) (i) $\dfrac{200 \div 40}{5}$ (ii) 1
   (c) (i) $\dfrac{4 \times 8}{8 \div 2}$ (ii) 8
4 (a) (i) 16 436   (ii) 18 000
   (b) (i) 24.96   (ii) 24
   (c) (i) 4.82 (3 s.f.)   (ii) 4
   (d) (i) 78.8 (3 s.f.)   (ii) 80
5 £17.02
6 5 packs
7 It is not possible to measure 6.6666 cm; 6.7 cm is more sensible.
8 (a) £29.38   (b) £58.74   (c) £10 293
9 Dress – £40, Skirt – £12.40, Suit – £66.66
10 (a) €4.50   (b) €3.75   (c) €2.48

Exercise 3A

1 (a) 2 : 1   (b) 5 : 2   (c) 3 : 1
   (d) 5 : 1   (e) 2 : 1
2 4 : 1
3 300 g
4 (a) £20 : £10   (b) 20 cm : 30 cm   (c) 250 g : 150 g
   (d) £3.75 : £6.25   (e) £7.50 : £5
5 (a) 20 boys   (b) 15 girls
6 (a) 5 managers   (b) 50 other workers
7 Louisa gets £25, Maria gets £35
8 £300 and £800
9 $3\frac{1}{8}$ litres of blue paint and $1\frac{7}{8}$ litres of yellow paint
10 Nick gets £3.60, Shawn gets £2.40

Exercise 3B

1 £40
2 £62.30
3 £1.20
4 £6.50
5 £17
6 625 g flour, 250 g margarine, 125 g sugar, 250 ml milk
7 10 magazines
8 6 CDs
9 10 pens
10 14 bottles

Exercise 3C

1 4 went swimming, 2 played squash
2 2 pens, 5 pencils
3 42 cm
4 1 cm, 5 cm, 5 cm; 3 cm, 4 cm, 4 cm; 5 cm, 3 cm, 3 cm
5 Student's own drawing, e.g.

3 cm

6 cm

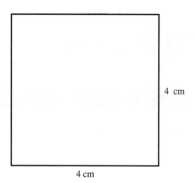

4 cm

4 cm

6 2 wins, 1 draw and 1 loss.
7 96 days
8 4 cups of tea and 4 cups of coffee.

Exercise 3D

1 2 : 1
2 (a) £24 : £16   (b) 50 cm : 30 cm   (c) £3.20 : £12.80
3 John gets £80, Kevin gets £70
4 10 girls
5 William gets £1.75, Mary gets £5.25
6 £4.80
7 £58.30
8 7 hours
9 4 biscuits and 2 cakes
10 3 cm and 12 cm

Exercise 4A

1 (a) 8.3   (b) 3.6   (c) 0.4
   (d) 15.1   (e) 8.0   (f) 5.0
   (g) 1000.1   (h) 0.6   (i) 50.1
2 (a) 10.06   (b) 8.45   (c) 0.01
   (d) 100.00   (e) 0.02   (f) 17.50
   (g) 29.46   (h) 0.06   (i) 2.45

Exercise 4B

1 (a) £43.60   (b) £40.95   (c) £61.36
   (d) £1.61   (e) £54.46
2 (a) 0.28   (b) 0.48   (c) 4.48
   (d) 56.95   (e) 40.95   (f) 2.46
3 17.78 m
4 £16.51
5 (a) 92.88   (b) 176.12   (c) 138.24

Exercise 4C

1 (a) (i) $1\frac{1}{4}$ hours   (ii) 1.25 hours
   (b) (i) $3\frac{3}{4}$ hours   (ii) 3.75 hours
   (c) (i) $4\frac{1}{2}$ hours   (ii) 4.5 hours
   (d) (i) $2\frac{1}{3}$ hours   (ii) 2.33 hours (2 d.p.)
   (e) (i) $3\frac{11}{12}$ hours   (ii) 3.92 hours (2 d.p.)
   (f) (i) $6\frac{1}{6}$ hours   (ii) 6.17 hours (2 d.p.)
2 (a) 6 boxes   (b) £10.80
3 $1\frac{1}{4}$ hours

Exercise 5A

1 $3p + 3q$ 2 $6a - 6b$ 3 $3x + 15$
4 $y^2 + 4y$ 5 $c^2 - c$ 6 $2ax + 3ay$
7 $5an - 4bn$ 8 $3t^2 + 7t$ 9 $2y^2 - 5y$
10 $6c^2 + c$ 11 $ap - bp$ 12 $px^2 - qx$

Exercise 5B

1 $2(x + 3y)$	**2** $5(2a - b)$	**3** $4(p + 3)$
4 $2(4c - 3d)$	**5** $3(4p + 3q)$	**6** $x(a + b)$
7 $a(2x - 3y)$	**8** $5(3t + 1)$	**9** $y(y + 2)$
10 $c(c - y)$	**11** $p(p + 6x)$	**12** $6(1 - 3q)$
13 $5(3d + 5)$	**14** $a(a - 3)$	**15** $x(7 + x)$
16 $p(4p - 5q)$	**17** $n(2n + 5)$	**18** $y(5y - 3)$
19 $x(2 - 3x)$	**20** $a(7a + 1)$	**21** $t(1 - 5t)$

Exercise 5C

1 8	**2** 8	**3** 6	**4** 0	**5** 70
6 26	**7** 5	**8** 0	**9** 21	**10** 30
11 0	**12** 23	**13** 9	**14** 4	**15** 10
16 66	**17** 10	**18** 90	**19** 40	**20** 18
21 25	**22** 18	**23** 15	**24** 16	**25** 9
26 9	**27** 45	**28** 26	**29** 73	**30** 27
31 9	**32** 1	**33** 125	**34** 54	**35** 48
36 34	**37** 64	**38** 125	**39** 19	**40** 1

Exercise 5D

1 1	**2** -11	**3** 11	**4** -3	**5** 8
6 -1	**7** -8	**8** -2	**9** 2	**10** 0
11 28	**12** -30	**13** 10	**14** -36	**15** -13
16 -18	**17** -30	**18** 54	**19** 60	**20** -12
21 -15	**22** -20	**23** 18	**24** -2	**25** 25
26 12	**27** 97	**28** 14	**29** 65	**30** 16
31 1	**32** 1	**33** 49	**34** 9	**35** 432
36 -375	**37** -48	**38** 32	**39** -11	**40** -27

Exercise 5E

1 (a) $6m + 6n$ (b) $5x - 5y$ (c) $4p - 4$
    (d) $t^2 + t$ (e) $q^2 - 5q$ (f) $2p^2 + pq$
    (g) $3ax + 4ay$ (h) $ac - bc^2$
2 (a) $5(x + 3y)$ (b) $3(5p - 3q)$ (c) $c(d + e)$
    (d) $x(x - 7)$ (e) $t(t + a)$ (f) $x(bx - 1)$
    (g) $p(3p + y)$ (h) $a(q^2 - t)$
3 (a) 11   (b) 21   (c) 0
    (d) 56   (e) 26   (f) 14
    (g) 24   (h) 0   (i) 98
    (j) 81   (k) 64   (l) 27
4 (a) 1   (b) 7   (c) 2
    (d) -6 (e) 8   (f) 24
    (g) -4 (h) 0   (i) -12
    (j) 12   (k) -6 (l) -128

Exercise 6A

1 $a = 5$	**2** $c = 10$	**3** $p = 7$
4 $d = 12$	**5** $x = 3$	**6** $b = 4$
7 $y = 0$	**8** $t = \frac{3}{5}$	**9** $q = 2\frac{1}{2}$
10 $n = 2\frac{2}{3}$	**11** $r = 3$	**12** $x = 5$
13 $c = 5$	**14** $p = 2$	**15** $c = 0$
16 $b = \frac{1}{2}$	**17** $d = 1\frac{2}{3}$	**18** $y = \frac{4}{5}$
19 $t = 2\frac{1}{3}$	**20** $w = 2\frac{1}{2}$	

Exercise 6B

1 $a = -4$	**2** $b = -6$	**3** $c = -1$
4 $d = -9$	**5** $e = -5\frac{1}{2}$	**6** $f = \frac{-5}{6}$
7 $g = -5\frac{2}{3}$	**8** $h = -2$	**9** $k = -1$
10 $m = \frac{-3}{4}$	**11** $n = -1\frac{3}{5}$	**12** $p = -2\frac{5}{6}$
13 $q = \frac{-2}{3}$	**14** $r = -4$	**15** $t = -2$
16 $u = -3$	**17** $v = \frac{-5}{6}$	**18** $w = -6\frac{1}{2}$
19 $x = \frac{-2}{3}$	**20** $y = -2\frac{1}{2}$	

Exercise 6C

1 $a = 4$	**2** $b = 8$	**3** $c = -1$
4 $d = \frac{3}{5}$	**5** $e = -3\frac{1}{2}$	**6** $f = \frac{3}{4}$
7 $g = 1\frac{2}{3}$	**8** $h = -12$	**9** $k = 2$
10 $m = \frac{3}{5}$	**11** $n = 5$	**12** $p = 3$
13 $q = -3$	**14** $r = \frac{2}{3}$	**15** $t = -1\frac{2}{3}$
16 $u = \frac{-3}{5}$	**17** $v = 2\frac{1}{2}$	**18** $w = -6$
19 $x = \frac{1}{8}$	**20** $y = -3\frac{2}{5}$	

Exercise 6D

1 $a = 4$	**2** $b = 7$	**3** $c = 6$
4 $d = 10$	**5** $e = \frac{1}{2}$	**6** $f = \frac{-2}{3}$
7 $g = 3\frac{2}{3}$	**8** $h = -1$	**9** $k = 1$
10 $m = 3$	**11** $n = 0$	**12** $p = 2$
13 $q = \frac{3}{4}$	**14** $r = -2$	**15** $t = 2\frac{1}{2}$

Exercise 6E

1 $a = 3$	**2** $b = 7$	**3** $c = 5$
4 $d = 7$	**5** $e = 6$	**6** $f = 3\frac{3}{7}$
7 $g = 1$	**8** $h = 0$	**9** $k = 2$
10 $m = 1$	**11** $n = \frac{1}{3}$	**12** $p = -4$
13 $q = -4$	**14** $r = 3\frac{2}{3}$	**15** $t = \frac{-3}{4}$

Exercise 6F

1 $a = 3$	**2** $b = 4$	**3** $c = 2\frac{1}{2}$
4 $d = -2$	**5** $d = \frac{1}{2}$	**6** $f = 0$
7 $g = \frac{-2}{3}$	**8** $f = 2\frac{3}{5}$	**9** $k = -1\frac{1}{2}$
10 $m = -5$	**11** $n = \frac{3}{5}$	**12** $p = -4\frac{2}{3}$

Exercise 6G

1 $a = 3$	**2** $b = 4$	**3** $c = 2$
4 $d = 5$	**5** $e = 0$	**6** $f = 2$
7 $g = 4$	**8** $h = 6$	**9** $k = 3$
10 $m = 0$	**11** $n = 7$	**12** $p = 5$
13 $q = \frac{5}{8}$	**14** $r = -4$	**15** $t = 3\frac{1}{2}$
16 $u = \frac{-2}{5}$	**17** $v = -2$	**18** $w = \frac{1}{3}$
19 $x = -1\frac{1}{2}$	**20** $y = 2\frac{3}{4}$	

Exercise 6H

1 $a = 3$	**2** $b = -2$	**3** $c = 3\frac{2}{3}$
4 $d = 2$	**5** $e = \frac{3}{4}$	**6** $f = -4$
7 $g = 4$	**8** $h = 2\frac{1}{2}$	**9** $k = \frac{-1}{6}$
10 $m = 2$	**11** $n = -1\frac{3}{4}$	**12** $p = 4$
13 $q = \frac{1}{2}$	**14** $r = -4\frac{1}{2}$	**15** $t = 1\frac{3}{4}$
16 $u = -3$	**17** $v = 1$	**18** $w = 0$
19 $x = \frac{-3}{10}$	**20** $y = -1\frac{2}{3}$	

Exercise 7A

1 (a) (i) $(7, 1)$ (ii) $(0, 3)$ (iii) $(7, 5)$
    (b) $(14, 3)$
    (c) (i) $(7, 3)$ (ii) $(10.5, 4)$
    (d) $x = 7$

2 (a)

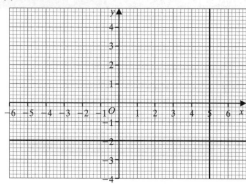

(b) $(5, -2)$

3 (a) (i) $(2, 3)$ **(ii)** $(-4, 3)$ **(iii)** $(-4, -1)$

(b)

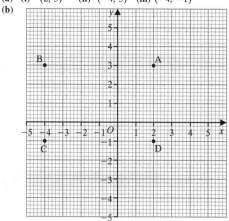

(c) $y = 3$

(d) $(-1, 1)$

Exercise 7B

1 (a) (b)

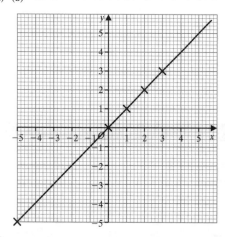

(c) $y = x$

2 $y = -x$

3 (a) (b)

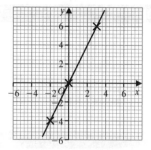

(c) $y = 2x$

4 (a) (b)

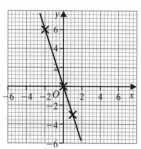

(c) $y = -3x$

5

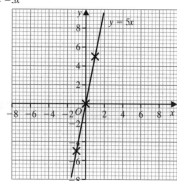

Exercise 7C

1 (a)

x	-3	-2	-1	0	1	2	3
$y = 2x + 3$	-3	-1	1	3	5	7	9

(b)

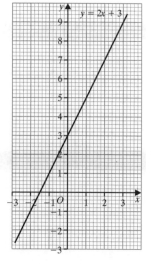

2 (a)

x	−6	−4	−2	0	2	4	6
y	2	3	4	5	6	7	8

(b)

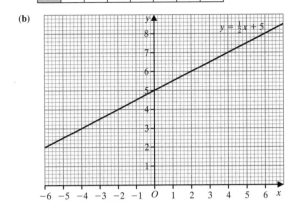

$y = \frac{1}{2}x + 5$

(c) (i) $y = 4.2$ **(ii)** $x = 3$

3 (a)

x		−2	−1	0	1	2	3
$y = 12 - 5x$		22	17	12	7	2	−3

(b)

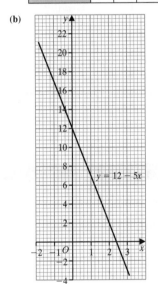

$y = 12 - 5x$

(c) $y = 6$
(d) (i) $x = 2.4$ **(ii)** $x = 0.4$

4

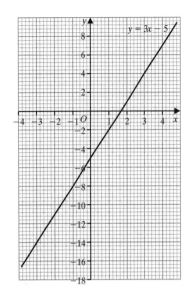

$y = 3x - 5$

5 (a)

x	−2	−1	0	1	2
$y = \frac{1}{2}x + 4$	3	$3\frac{1}{2}$	4	$4\frac{1}{2}$	5

(b)

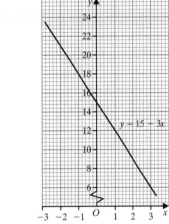

$y = \frac{1}{2}x + 4$

6

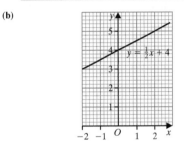

$y = 15 - 3x$

7

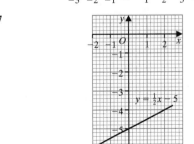

$y = \frac{1}{2}x - 5$

8

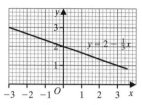

9 (a)

x	−4	−3	−2	−1	0	1	2	3
y	−7	−5	−3	−1	1	3	5	7

(b) (c)

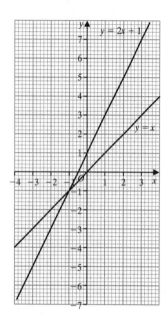

(d) $(−1, −1)$

Exercise 7D

1 (a) 62 miles
 (b) 388 km
 (c) France's is greater, by 4 miles per hour or 7 kilometres per hour
2 (a) £35
 (b)

Miles	50	100	150	200	250	300
Total cost (£)	25	35	45	55	65	75

 (c)

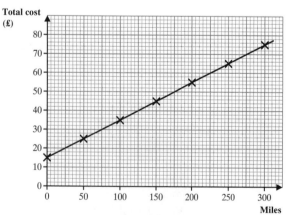

 (d) $y = 15 + 0.2x$
 (e) 125 miles

3 (a) 33 litres
 (b) 9.1 gallons
 (c) 163.8 gallons
4 (a)

Hours	1	2	3	4	5	6	7	8
Total charge (£)	37	49	61	73	85	97	109	121

 (b)

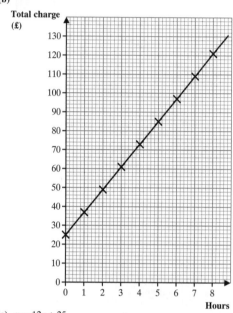

 (c) $y = 12x + 25$
 (d) $4\frac{1}{2}$ hours

Exercise 7E

1 Lester started from rest, accelerating for the first two seconds to reach his maximum speed. He then sprinted at a constant speed for about 6 seconds. He slowed down slightly for the last two seconds of the sprint, probably due to tiredness.

2

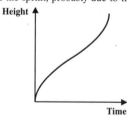

3 (a) £400
 (b) The overall trend is an increase in Gemma's gas bill.
4 (a) 60 m
 (b) 10 m
 (c) 6.8 m

Exercise 8A

1 $a = 52°$ (corresponding angles)
2 $b = 38°$ (corresponding angles)
3 $c = 124°$ (alternate angles)
4 $d = 47°$ (corresponding angles, angles on a straight line)
5 $e = 140°$ (corresponding angles, angles on a straight line)
6 $f = 121°$ (corresponding angles, angles on a straight line)
 $g = 59°$ (corresponding angles)
 $h = 59°$ (opposite angles)
7 $i = 102°$ (corresponding anles, angles on a straight line)
 $j = 78°$ (corresponding angles)

8 $k = 78°$ (angles in a triangle, angles on a straight line)
$m = 102°$ (corresponding angles, angles on a straight line)
$n = 143°$ (corresponding angles, angles on a straight line)
9 **(a)** $x = 109°$ (angles on a straight line)
  (b) angle $P\widehat{Q}S = 24°$ (alternate angles)
10 $x = 30°$

Exercise 8B

1 Angle ABE = angle $BCD = a$ (corresponding angles)
angle DBE = angle $BDC = b$ (alternate angles)
So, angle ABD = angle ABE + angle $DBE = a + b$
2 Angle XBZ = angle $ACB = b$ (alternate angles)
angle XBY = angle $ACB = c$ (corresponding angles)
So, angle YBZ = angle XBZ + angle $XBY = b + c$
3 **(a)** angle $BAC = x$
  (b) angle ACX = angle $BAC = x$ (alternate angles)
  So AC bisects angle BCX
4 Angle BDC = angle $ABD = x$ (alternate angles)
angle ADB = angle $CBD = y$ (alternate angles)
So, angle $A = 180° - x - y$ = angle C (angles in a triangle)
5 Angle $ABX = 54°$ (corresponding angles)
angle $CBY = 54°$ (opposite angles)
6 Angle BCY = angle SYX = angle $QXW = 48°$ (all corresponding angles)
angle RCD = angle $BCY = 48°$ (opposite angles)
7 Angle CBX = angle BXC (equal angles of an isosceles triangle)
angle D = angle CBX (opposite angles of a parallelogram)
So, angle D = angle BXC
8 Angle BCS = angle $ABQ = 40°$ (corresponding angles)
angle $DCS = 140°$ (angles on a straight line)
So, angle $CSD = 20°$ (angles in a triangle and CDS is isosceles)

Exercise 8C

1
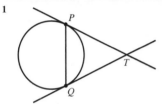

PQ is a chord.
PQT is an isosceles triangle.

2
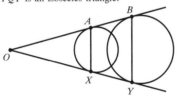

AX and BY are parallel.

3
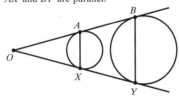

AX and BY are parallel.

Exercise 8D

1
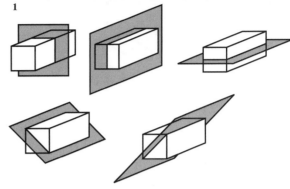

2 9 planes
(1 parallel to each pair of parallel faces, total of 3, and 1 through each pair of opposite edges, total of 6)
3 **(a)** 2 planes   **(b)** 1 plane   **(c)** 2 planes
  (d) 4 planes   **(e)** 1 plane
4
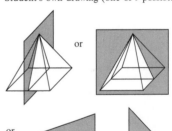
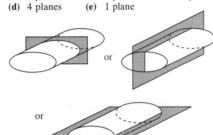

5 **(i)** Student's own drawing (one of 9 possible planes)
  (ii)
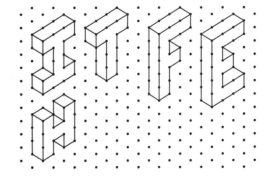

Exercise 8E

1 Possible answers are:
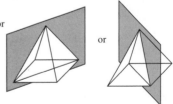

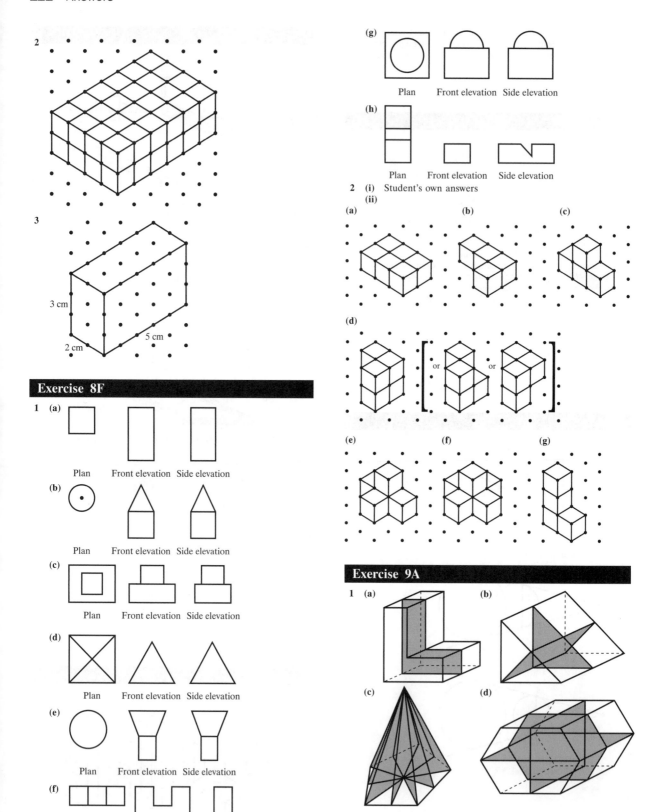

2

3

3 cm
2 cm
5 cm

Exercise 8F

1 (a)
Plan   Front elevation   Side elevation

(b)
Plan   Front elevation   Side elevation

(c)
Plan   Front elevation   Side elevation

(d)
Plan   Front elevation   Side elevation

(e)
Plan   Front elevation   Side elevation

(f)
Plan   Front elevation   Side elevation

(g)
Plan   Front elevation   Side elevation

(h)
Plan   Front elevation   Side elevation

2 (i) Student's own answers
(ii)

(a)   **(b)**   **(c)**

(d)
or   or

(e)   **(f)**   **(g)**

Exercise 9A

1 (a)   **(b)**

(c)   **(d)**

2 **(a)** **(b)**

3 **(a)** **(b)**

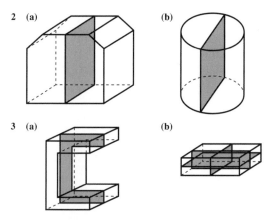

1 plane   3 planes

Exercise 9B

1 **(a)** 3 km **(b)** 1.5 km
  (c) 2.25 km **(d)** 3.75 km
  (e) 4.3 km **(f)** 6.05 km
2 **(a)** Measurements of sides, clockwise from top side:
    7 cm, 1 cm, 3 cm, 4 cm, 10 cm, 5 cm
  (b)

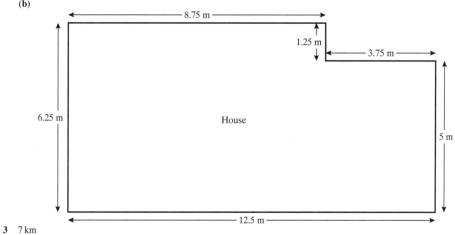

3 7 km

4 **(a)** 2.5 km
  (b) Diagram should be twice the size of map in question
     e.g.

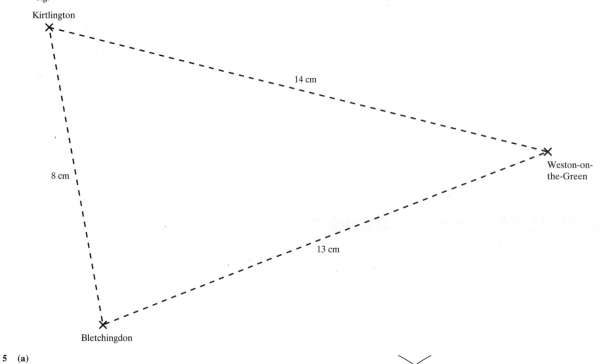

5 **(a)**

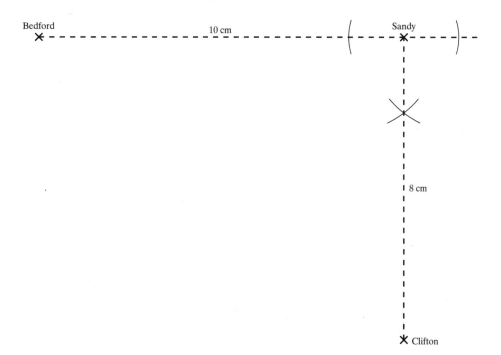

  (b) Measured distance = 12.8 cm (1 d.p.)
     so real distance = 12.8 km (1 d.p.)

10.1 Activity

(a) (i) Circles – **A**, **F**, **G**
Squares – **B**, **E**, **I**, **K**
Rectangles – **C**, **D**, **H**, **J**

    (ii) **A → F** : enlargement, scale factor 2
A → G : enlargement, scale factor 3
F → G : enlargement, scale factor 1.5
B → E : enlargement, scale factor $\frac{1}{2}$
B → I : enlargement, scale factor 2
B → K : enlargement, scale factor 1.5
E → I : enlargement, scale factor 4
E → K : enlargement, scale factor 3
I → K : enlargement, scale factor $\frac{3}{4}$

(b) **A**, **F**, **G** are similar to each other (circles are similar).
B, **E**, **I**, **K** are similar to each other (squares are similar).
C, **D**, **H**, **J** are not similar to any other shape.

Exercise 10A

1 (a) **A** and **B**, SSS
(b) **A** and **C**, SAS
(c) **A** and **C**, ASA
(d) **A** and **C**, RHS

2 (a) Yes, SAS
(b) No
(c)
(d) Yes, ASA
(e) Yes, SAS

3 (a)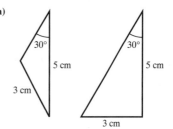

(b)

Exercise 10B

1 (a)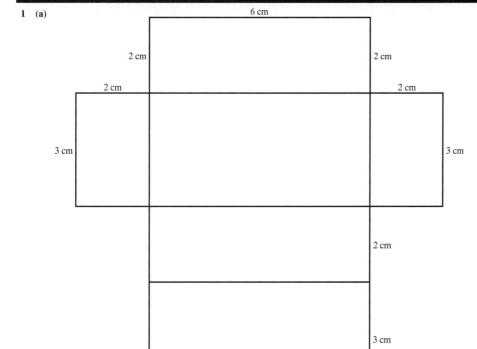

(b) Half size:

(c)

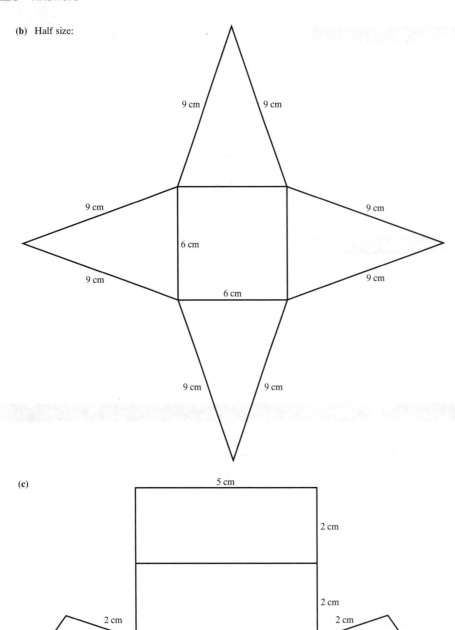

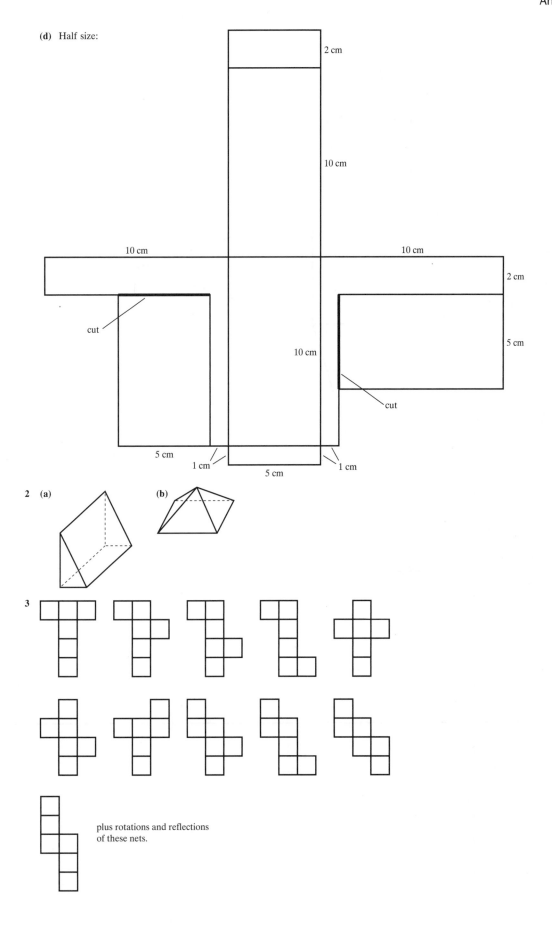

(d) Half size:

2 cm

10 cm

10 cm   10 cm

2 cm

cut

5 cm

10 cm

cut

5 cm

1 cm   1 cm

5 cm

2 (a)   (b)

3

plus rotations and reflections
of these nets.

4 (a)

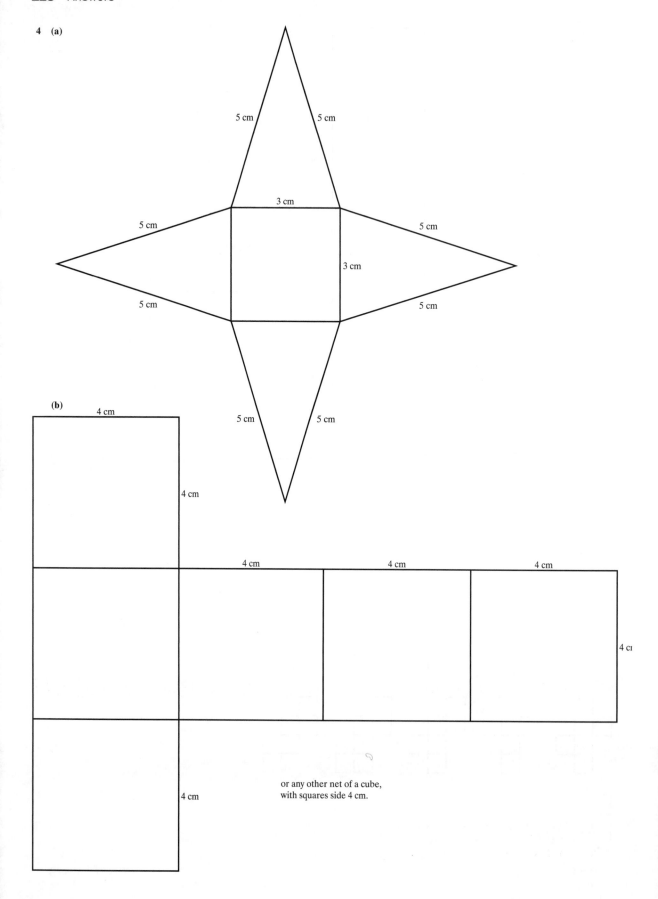

(b)

or any other net of a cube,
with squares side 4 cm.

(c)

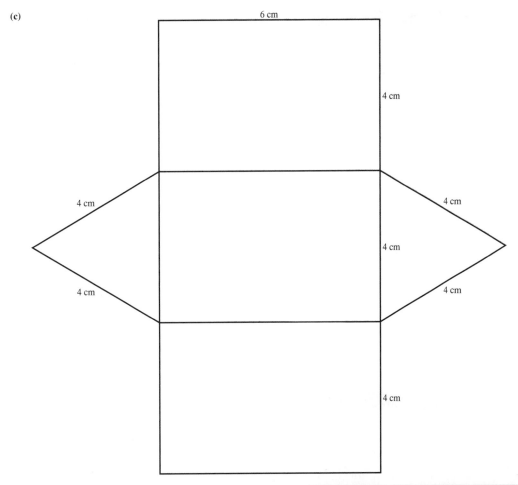

5 Possible answer:

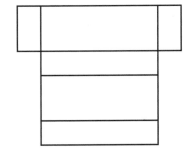

1 (a) 15.4 lbs   (b) 48.4 lbs   (c) 86.24 lbs
   (d) 8.954 lbs   (e) 1.32 lbs
2 (a) 1.36 kg (2 d.p.)   (b) 68.18 kg (2 d.p.)
   (c) 43.86 lbs (2 d.p.)   (d) 11 kg
   (e) 0.45 kg (2 d.p.)
3 80.9 kg (1 d.p.)
4 379.2 km
5 26.25 miles
6 26 full bottles
7 353.7p per gallon
8 1325 g
9 6 ft
10 167.5 cm

1 (a) 50 000   (b) 280 000
   (c) 12 000   (d) 1 050 000
   (e) 2.6   (f) 0.34
   (g) 800   (h) 2200
   (i) 24   (j) 362
2 (a) 2 300 000   (b) 40 000
   (c) 304 000   (d) 7
   (e) 0.53   (f) 0.0265
   (g) 4000   (h) 13 050
   (i) 8.4   (j) 0.43
3 (a) (i)   6.3 m^2 (ii)   63 000 cm^2
   (b) (i)   0.882 m^3 (ii)   882 000 cm^3

1 (a) Circumference = 37.7 cm, area = 113 cm^2 (3 s.f.)
   (b) $C = 88.0$ cm, $A = 616$ cm^2 (3 s.f.)
   (c) $C = 52.2$ cm, $A = 216$ cm^2 (3 s.f.)
   (d) $C = 4.65$ cm, $A = 1.72$ m^2 (3 s.f.)
   (e) $C = 35.5$ cm, $A = 100$ cm^2 (3 s.f.)
   (f) $C = 43.7$ mm, $A = 152$ mm^2 (3 s.f.)
   (g) $C = 5.03$ m, $A = 2.01$ m^2 (3 s.f.)
2 4.91 cm^2 (3 s.f.)
3 Diameter = 7.96 m (3 s.f.), area = 49.7 m^2 (3 s.f.)
4 201 cm

Exercise 11D

1

	Distance	Time	Average speed
(a)	128 km	2 h	64 km/h
(b)	58 miles	$7\frac{1}{4}$ h	8 mph
(c)	600 m	20 s	30 m/s
(d)	2.3 km	50 s	46 m/s
(e)	175 miles	$3\frac{1}{2}$ h	50 mph
(f)	165 km	$2\frac{1}{2}$ h	66 km/h
(g)	750 m	30 s	25 m/s
(h)	6 km	$2\frac{1}{2}$ h	40 m/s
(i)	100 km	50 min	120 km/h
(j)	254 miles	1 h 15 min	203.2 mph
(k)	76 km	5 h 4 min	15 km/h
(l)	27.15 km	16 min 10 s	101 km/h
(m)	127 miles	2 h 18 min 33 s	55 mph
(n)	99 miles	3 h 18 min	30 mph
(o)	2350 km	$1\frac{1}{2}$ days	65.3 km/h

2 129 miles
3 51.0 mph (3 s.f.)
4 10.8 m/s (3 s.f.)
5 3 h 27 min 16 s (nearest second)
6 7200 m or 7.2 km
7 6.07 km (3 s.f)
8 4 h 37 min 30 s
9 9 h 3 min 15 s (nearest second)
10 28.3 mph (3 s.f.)

Exercise 12A

1 (a)

	100 g	200 g	300 g	Total
Ground	15	50	35	100
Powder	80	40	20	140
Granules	40	50	70	160
Total	135	140	125	400

(b) (i) 40   **(ii)** 15
(c)

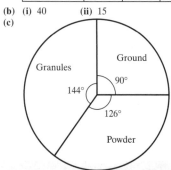

2

	KS3	KS4	Sixth Form	Total
Walk				
Cycle				
Car				
Bus				
Total				

3 (a)

	UK	Europe	Elsewhere	Total
July	12	20	8	40
August	36	48	16	100
September	8	32	20	60
Total	56	100	44	200

(b)

September 108°
July 72°
180°
August

(c)

Elsewhere 79°
UK 101°
180°
Europe

4

	Front Stalls	Rear Stalls	Front Circle	Rear Circle	Total
Adults	20	20	80	30	150
Children	40	32	58	10	140
Senior Citizens	10	0	40	60	110
Total	70	52	178	100	400

Exercise 12B

1 **(a)** **(b)**

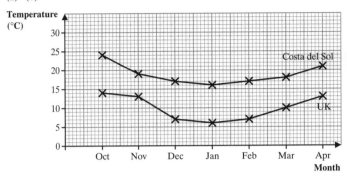

(c) November
(d) 8.86 °C (2 d.p.)

2 **(a)** **(b)**

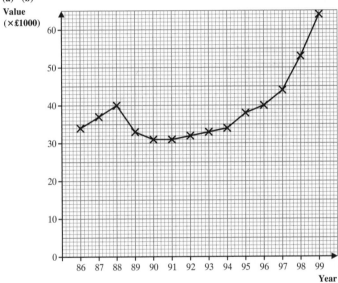

(c) Between 1986 and 1988 the value increased steadily.
Between 1988 and 1989 the value sharply decreased, to
lower than the value when Asif and Wendy bought the
house.
The value of the house was lowest in 1990 and 1991, but
between 1991 and 1994 the value slowly increased.
Between 1994 and 1999 the value increased very sharply,
and from 1995 it increased by more each year, to its
highest point in 1999.

3 **(a)** **(b)**

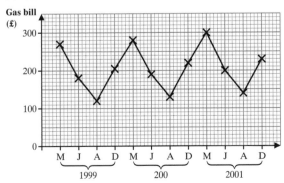

(c) In each year the gas bill decreased from March to August.
In each year the gas bill increased from August to March
of the next year.
Comparing the same months in different years we see that
the overall trend is an increase in the gas bill over the
three years.

Exercise 12C

1 £14 206.40
2 66p
3 Assuming bread prices follow the changes in the RPI, a similar
loaf would cost 5p
4 **(a)**

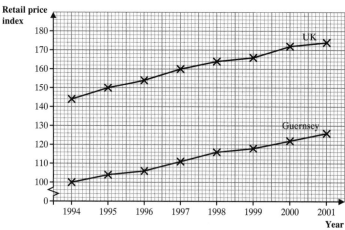

(b) (c)

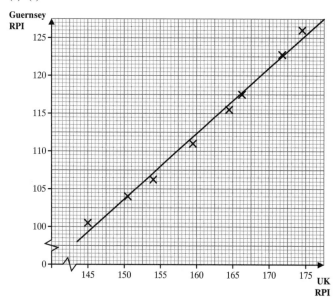

(d) Scatter diagram shows positive correlation between the UK
and Guernsey RPIs
(e) Proportional changes to RPI have been:

For UK: $\dfrac{174.6}{145.0} = 1.204$ For Guernsey: $\dfrac{125.9}{100.2} = 1.256$

Change in RPI is less for UK than for Guernsey.
So, no evidence to support claim.

Exercise 12D

1 (a)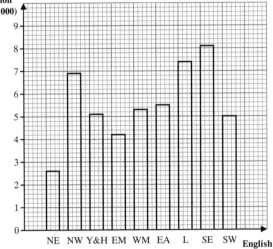

Population
(×1 000 000)

English regions

(b)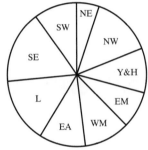

(c) South East

(d) £52 500, £61 000, £65 000, £68 850, £76 200, £82 500,
£88 800, £120 000, £147 500

(e) (f)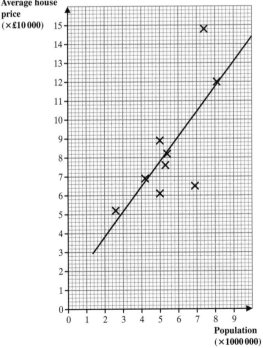

Average house
price
(×£10 000)

Population
(×1 000 000)

(g) There is a positive correlation between house prices and
population.

2 **(a)**   **(i)**   **(ii)**

Age range	Number of people to nearest million	Number of people to nearest hundred thousand
Under 5 yrs	19 000 000	19 200 000
5 to 9 yrs	21 000 000	20 500 000
10 to 14 yrs	21 000 000	20 500 000
15 to 19 yrs	20 000 000	20 200 000
20 to 24 yrs	19 000 000	19 000 000
25 to 34 yrs	40 000 000	39 900 000
35 to 44 yrs	45 000 000	45 100 000
45 to 54 yrs	38 000 000	37 700 000
55 to 59 yrs	13 000 000	13 500 000
60 to 64 yrs	11 000 000	10 800 000
65 to 74 yrs	18 000 000	18 400 000
75 to 84 yrs	12 000 000	12 400 000
85 yrs and over	4 000 000	4 200 000

(b)

Number of people
per 5 year interval
to nearest million
(×1 000 000)

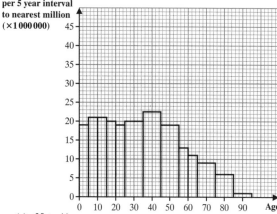

(c) 35 to 44 years

3 The mode grade in 2000 was C.
The mode grade in 2001 was B.
The percentage of students getting grades A*–B has gone up
from 36% in 2000 to 39% in 2001.

4 **(a)** 1 348 000 000, is much larger than the other populations.
(b) The median would truly reflect the average population.
The mean will not since the exceptional value will affect it.
It does not make sense to use the mode since the data is
not grouped.

(c)

0	2 3 4 4 4 5 5 9
1	0 0 0 0 3 6
2	2
3	8 9
4	1 5 9
5	8 9
6	0
7	0
8	2
9	
10	0
11	
12	7
13	
14	2 7
15	
16	
17	6
⋮	
28	7
⋮	
134	8

(d) Out of the seven countries Uruguay has the largest
number of wins per million people; we expect that the
higher this is, the better the country is at football. Despite
having a small population, Uruguay have found footballers
good enough to win the World Cup two times.

Exercise 13A

1 **(a)** Black, since there is the least number of these.
    (b) $\frac{3}{10}$
    (c) **(i)** $\frac{2}{5}$ **(ii)** $\frac{7}{10}$
         (iii) $\frac{11}{20}$ **(iv)** 0
2 **(a)** 0.998
    (b) Probability of being cracked = 0.002
    So the most likely number of eggs to be cracked
         = 140 000 × 0.002
         = 280 eggs
3 $\frac{14}{15}$
4 0.09
5 0.21
6 29 times
7 **(a)**

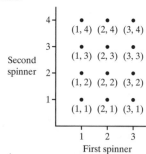

(b) $\frac{1}{12}$
(c) **(i)** $\frac{1}{4}$ **(ii)** $\frac{1}{2}$ **(iii)** $\frac{1}{2}$
8 360 words

Terminal practice paper 1

1 **(a)** 23   **(b)** 252   **(c)** 400
2 **(a)** $\frac{4}{5}$ **(b)** 80%
3 **(a)**

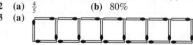

(b)

Shape number	1	2	3	4	5
Number of matchsticks	4	10	16	22	28

(c) 64

(d) All shapes have an even number of matchsticks in them, so there cannot be a shape with 365 matchsticks in it.

4 (a) Cuboid   **(b)** Cylinder   **(c)** Cone

5 (a) 200   **(b)** 7

6 (a) Pounds or ounces

(b) Gallons

(c) Inches

7 (a) 175 minutes   **(b)** $T = 25(w + 1)$

8

Blood group	Tally	Frequency
A	⅃⅃⅃ ⅃⅃⅃ ‖	12
B	‖‖	3
AB	‖	2
O	⅃⅃⅃ ⅃⅃⅃ ‖‖	13

9 (a) £49   **(b)** 56

10 (a)

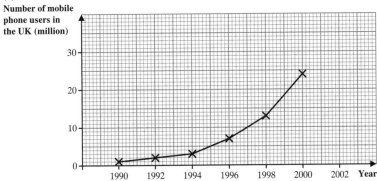

Number of mobile phone users in the UK (million)

(b) 18 million

(c) 42 milliom

11 Estimate for length of car = 3 m
Since, estimate for height of average woman = 1.5 m, and according to the picture the car is about twice as long as the woman is tall.

12 (a) 182.75 g   **(b)** 28 kg

13 (a) (3, 7)   **(b)** $(2, 5\frac{1}{2})$

14 (a) $\frac{3}{10}$ **(b)** $\frac{7}{20}$

15 (a) 35 miles   **(b)** 67 000 cm²

16 0.03

17 $x = 1\frac{1}{2}$

Terminal practice paper 2

1 (a) £3.60   **(b)** 11 bottles

2 (a) 192   **(b)** 12

3 (a)

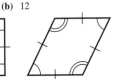

(b) Square, rhombus

4 (a) £1.09   **(b)** £2.16   **(c)** 450 g

5 (a) (i) 115 New Zealand dollars

(ii) £19

(b) 680 New Zealand dollars. £50 converts to 170 New Zealand dollars, so £200 = 4 × £50 converts to 4 × 170 = 680 New Zealand dollars.

6 (a) 11 °C   **(b)** 5 °C   **(c)** −13 °C

7 (a) (i) £127.77

(ii) £2132.96

(iii) 53.3% (1 d.p.)

(b) 60 months

(c) £3000

8 96.623
9 (a) $x = -2$ (b) $5y - 20$ (c) $t(t - 6)$
10 (a) (i) 2 (ii) 2
(b) (i) 63° (ii) Acute
11 35.75 grams
12 (a) 8 cm³
(b)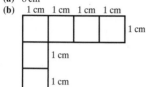
13 79 kg
14

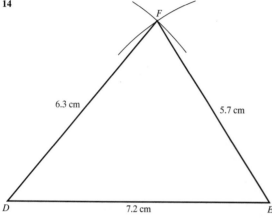

15 (a) Angle $C = 75°$ since angles in a triangle add up to 180°.
Angle A = Angle C, so ABC is isosceles
(b) The angle y and angle 68° are alternate angles and so are equal.
16 (a) They were 3% lower.
(b) £91 800